THE AMAZING
TRIVIA QUIZ
CHALLENGE

THE AMAZING TRIVIA QUIZ CHALLENGE

Cosmo Brown

Bath · New York · Singapore · Hong Kong · Cologne · Delhi · Melbourne

This edition published by Parragon in 2010

Parragon
Queen Street House
4 Queen Street
Bath BA1 1HE, UK

Copyright © Parragon Books Ltd 2009

Designed & produced by Design Principals, Warminster

Compiled by Cosmo Brown

ISBN: 978-1-4454-0545-2

Printed in Malaysia

CONTENTS

ART & LITERATURE
WORDS AND PICTURES (1)

1

Which Brontë sister wrote the novel *Jane Eyre*?
Charl

2

Who painted the ceiling of the Sistine Chapel?
Michaelangelo

3

Who commanded the *Nautilus* in Jules Verne's classic tale?

4

Which 19thC US artist famously painted the American West?
Remington

5

In John Steinbeck's *Travels with Charley*, what was Charley?

6

Who wrote *For Whom the Bell Tolls*?
E. Hem

7

Which museum is home to the *Mona Lisa*?
Louvre

8

Name the third part of the *Lord of the Rings* trilogy.

9

Who is the creator of Discworld?
W. Disn

10

What do the initials stand for in J K Rowling?
Joanne

11

What was the first James Bond book?
Goldfinger

12

Larry McMurtry's best-selling novel *Lonesome* ... *Dove*

ART & LITERATURE
CHILDREN'S BOOKS

1

Who created *The Cat in the Hat?*

Dr Seuss

2

Who first illustrated *Alice's Adventures in Wonderland?*

3

Blind Pew is a character in which children's classic?

Alice

4

Which is the third book in the *Harry Potter* series?

G Gob

5

Hugh Lofting created which famous children's character?

6

In *Peter Pan*, what are the names of Wendy's brothers?

Michael John

7

Big fat Christ

What does "BFG" stand for in Roald Dahl's story?

8

Baum

Who wrote *The Wonderful Wizard of Oz?*

9

Spider

Who does Charlotte save in *Charlotte's Web?*

wilber

10

Flopsy Mopsy Cotton

Name the rabbit trio in *The Tales of Peter Rabbit*.

11

Red Balloon

What children's classic was written by Antoine de Saint-Exupéry?

12

What are the Grimm Brothers' first names?

ART & LITERATURE
MODERN ART

1

Which modern artist did Ed Harris portray on film in 2000

2

In which year did Pablo Picasso die – 1953, 1963 or 1973?

3

Which bombed Spanish town inspired a Picasso painting?

4

Who turned a can of soup into a work of art?

5

Who created the Beatles' "Sgt Pepper" album cover?

6

What is the image in Jasper Johns' painting *Flag*?

7

Which American artist painted *Nighthawks*?

8

Which British painter is the grandson of Sigmund Freud?

9

What nationality was the painter Joan Miró?

10

In which country was Francis Bacon born?

11

Constantin Brancusi was famous in which art form?

12

Which artist was expelled from the Surrealist movement in 1939?

ART & LITERATURE
POETS AND POETRY

1

Which poet was married to fellow poet Ted Hughes?

2

Who wrote "The Rime of the Ancient Mariner"?

3

Which poet wrote *Leaves of Grass*?

4

What was lost and regained in the poems of John Milton?

5

What poem begins: "I wandered lonely as a cloud"?

6

Which prolific US 19th-century poetess lived as a recluse?

7

What do the initials in W H Auden stand for?

8

Which poet's only novel was entitled *The Bell Jar*?

9

To which bird did John Keats compose an ode?

10

Which English poem ends: "And is there honey still for tea?"

11

What was Percy Shelley's middle name?

12

Whose poems appeared on a postage stamp in 2002?

ART & LITERATURE
FAMOUS PEN NAMES

1

How is Charles Lutwidge Dodgson better known?

2

Which best-selling author is David Cornwell?

3

What was Samuel Langhorne Clemens' more famous name?

4

How was Theodore Seuss Geisel better known?

5

Which 18th-century French writer was François Marie Arouet?

6

Mary Westmacott is a pen name of which famous author?

7

William Sydney Porter wrote short stories under which name?

8

What was the pen name of Eric Blair?

9

Mary Ann Evans is the real name of which 19thC English novelist?

10

What was the pen name of Baroness Karen Blixen?

11

Under what name did Emily Brontë first publish *Wuthering Heights*?

12

Frederic Dannay and Manfred B Lee are which mystery writer?

ART & LITERATURE
WORDS AND PICTURES (2)

1

Who wrote *Of Mice and Men*?

2

Which French impressionist painter was born in the Virgin Islands?

3

What did the crocodile swallow in *Peter Pan*?

4

Who is the artist son of painter Andrew Wyeth?

5

Who wrote the novel *Jurassic Park*?

6

Which artist's Pink Period followed his Blue Period?

7

How many books are there in the New Testament?

8

Who is *The Hobbit* referred to in the title?

9

Who wrote *The Hitchhiker's Guide to the Galaxy*?

10

What was the artist Raphael's real name?

11

What does the F stand for in F Scott Fitzgerald?

12

The Kiss is a famous sculpture by which artist?

1

In which English town was Charles Dickens born?

2

Which Dickens novel was unfinished at his death?

3

Uriah Heep is a character in which novel?

4

What is the Artful Dodger's real name?

5

With which actress did Charles Dickens have an affair?

6

What are the two cities in *A Tale of Two Cities*?

7

Which Dickens character lent her name to an umbrella?

8

In which novel is Thomas Gradgrind a character?

9

Name Scrooge's deceased partner in *A Christmas Carol*.

10

Where was Little Dorrit born?

11

Who was the headmaster of Dotheboys Hall?

12

Which Dickens novel revolves around the Gordon Riots?

ART & LITERATURE
WHO PAINTED THESE?

1

The Blue Boy

2

Girl with a Pearl Earring

3

The Dance Class

4

The Creation of the Heavens

5

The Kiss

6

The Last Supper

7

The Scream

8

The Umbrellas

9

The Water-Lily Pond

10

The Starry Night

11

The Garden of Earthly Delights

12

At the Moulin Rouge

ART & LITERATURE
CLASSIC CHARACTERS

1

Name the Three Musketeers.

2

Who is Quasimodo?

3

Which classic begins: "Call me Ishmael"?

4

What was Madame Bovary's first name?

5

In which Jane Austen novel does Colonel Brandon feature?

6

Who lived at 221b Baker Street?

7

Who is the heroine of William Thackeray's *Vanity Fair*?

8

What is the name of Don Quixote's horse?

9

In which Russian novel is Raskolnikov the central character?

10

In *Gulliver's Travels*, what is Gulliver's first name?

11

Hester Prynne is the central character in which American novel?

12

Who was the last of the Mohicans?

1

Who created the aristocratic detective Lord Peter Wimsey?

2

In which novel does private eye Philip Marlowe first appear?

3

Inspector Lestrade is constantly outdone by which super sleuth?

4

Who is the teenage detective of River Heights?

5

Who solves the mystery of *The Murders of the Rue Morgue*?

6

In which precinct did Ed McBain set many stories?

7

Which hard-boiled private eye calls his gun "Betsy"?

8

In which country does Inspector Napoleon Bonaparte pursue crime?

9

What nationality is Hercule Poirot?

10

Which crime writer worked for the Pinkerton Detective Agency?

11

Who created private eye Lew Archer?

12

What is the name of the inquiring monk in *The Name of the Rose*?

ART & LITERATURE
WORDS AND PICTURES (3)

1

What is France's top literary prize?

2

Where is the Prado museum?

3

What nationality is the writer Margaret Atwood?

4

Who wrote twelve volumes about Casanova?

5

What painting is also known as *La Giaconda*?

6

Who wrote *The Age of Innocence*?

7

What do sculptors make as a preliminary model?

8

Which American poet was charged with treason in 1945?

9

What is the term for a wall painting?

10

What was Jane Austen's first published novel?

11

Whose novel *Summer Crossing* was published posthumously in 2005?

12

Which artist/naturalist illustrated *The Birds of America*?

ART & LITERATURE
WHO WROTE THESE NOVELS?

1

Peter Pan

2

Persuasion

3

Tom Jones

4

Jaws

5

Vanity Fair

6

The Girl with the Dragon Tattoo

7

Moby Dick

8

The Invisible Man

9

The Three Musketeers

10

Dracula

11

The Autobiography of Alice B Toklas

12

The Red Badge of Courage

ART & LITERATURE
ARTISTS IN THE FRAME

1

Who put America on the cover of the *Saturday Evening Post*?

2

Which Italian artist's name means "little barrel"?

3

Who turned his garden at Giverny into an artistic endeavor?

4

Which French painter lived and worked in Tahiti?

5

In which country was Marc Chagall born?

6

How was the artist Raffaello Santi better known?

7

Which famous artist was at home at the Moulin Rouge?

8

Whose Pink Period followed his Blue Period?

9

In which century was Michelangelo born?

10

Which Flemish painter was knighted by Charles I?

11

What name was Domenikos Theotocopoulos known by?

12

Which artist wrote *The Gentle Art of Making Enemies*?

ART & LITERATURE
ALL ABOUT THE BARD

1

Who was William Shakespeare's wife?

2

Who is warned: "Beware the ides of March"?

3

On which Shakespeare play is the musical *Kiss Me Kate* based?

4

What war is the background to *Troilus and Cressida*?

5

In which play is Leontes king of Sicily?

6

Who are the rival families in *Romeo and Juliet*?

7

Which play is set in one place and takes place all in one day?

8

Which play has "Athens" in the title?

9

Shakespeare's birthday is on which saint's day?

10

In which forest is *As You Like It* set?

11

What are the names of King Lear's three daughters?

12

Complete the title of Shakespeare's poem: "The Rape of . . . ".

ART & LITERATURE
WORDS AND PICTURES (4)

1

Whose first novel was *High Fidelity*?

2

What is Lascaux in France famous for?

3

Which pier features in a George Orwell book title?

4

How many parts to a triptych?

5

Which revolutionary arts movement was founded in 1916?

6

Which Alexandre Dumas was the novelist—father or son?

7

Which French sculptor created The Statue of Liberty?

8

Name the five Bennet girls in *Pride and Prejudice*.

9

Who wrote the philosophical work, *The Republic*?

10

Who is the captain of the *Pequod* in *Moby Dick*?

11

Which Flemish artist became court painter to Charles I?

12

Which Russian writer died at a railway station?

1

Who wrote "Hiawatha"?

2

Who recited one of his poems at JFK's inauguration in 1961?

3

What do the initials stand for in T S Eliot?

4

How many lines in a sonnet?

5

Which poet was awarded the Presidential Medal of Arts in 2000?

6

Which Irish poet won the Nobel Prize for Literature in 1995?

7

Which poet is the subject of the movie *Bright Star*?

8

Which W H Auden poem was read in *Four Weddings and a Funeral*?

9

The poem "The Defense of Fort McHenry" became which anthem?

10

What was Lord Byron's first name?

11

Which poet did Spanish Nationalists murder in 1936?

12

Which poet jumped to a watery grave in 1932?

1

Which playwright won the Nobel Prize for Literature in 2005?

2

The Cocktail Party and *The Family Reunion* are by whom?

3

The *Emperor Jones* was whose first major stage success?

4

On which play is the musical *My Fair Lady* based?

5

In which play is Blanche DuBois a key character?

6

Who wrote the Oedipus trilogy?

7

In which country was Tom Stoppard born?

8

Which famous playwright was stabbed to death in London in 1593?

9

Which "Monologues" are all about women?

10

Who wrote *Caesar and Cleopatra*?

11

Which Arthur Miller play has witchcraft as its theme?

12

Oscar Wilde and Bernard Shaw were born in which country?

ART & LITERATURE
OLD MASTERS

1

With which European city is Canaletto most famously associated?

2

Who painted *The Naked Maja*?

3

Which French Impressionist painted *Westminster Bridge* in 1871?

4

William Hogarth's *A Rake's Progress* comprises how many paintings?

5

Who was Dante Gabriel Rossetti's poet sister?

6

Whose painting, *Irises,* sold for $49m at auction in 1987?

7

Who painted the execution of Emperor Maximilian of Mexico?

8

In Botticelli's *The Birth of Venus*, what is Venus standing on?

9

A 19th-century French artist noted for his ballet paintings?

10

Which Pre-Raphaelite artist painted *Ophelia*?

11

The Spanish artist Diego Velazquez died in which century?

12

Who was the foremost artist of the French Revolution?

1

What fantasy kingdom is just through the wardrobe?

2

Which fictional doctor lived in Puddleby-on-Marsh?

3

In which English classic will you find Brobdingnag?

4

What has London become in George Orwell's *1984*?

5

In *Mork and Mindy*, from which planet does Mork come?

6

Which writer created Yoknapatawpha County?

7

Who is Neverland's most famous resident?

8

Which English humorist created the Drones Club?

9

In whose stories does the town of Lake Wobegon feature?

10

In which 1930s classic can Shangri-La be found?

11

What is the name of Professor Challenger's lost world?

12

Where was *Gulliver's Travels* author Jonathan Swift born?

ART & LITERATURE
20TH-CENTURY CLASSICS

1

Who wrote *Watership Down*?

2

What begins: "Last night I dreamt I went to Manderley again"?

3

Who was Lady Chatterley's lover?

4

The Tin Drum is by which German author?

5

Who is the narrator in the novel *Lolita*?

6

Which Evelyn Waugh novel is a satire on Fleet Street?

7

Napoleon and Snowball are characters in which political novel?

8

Don DeLillo's *Libra* is about which alleged assassin?

9

Holden Caulfield is the hero of which novel?

10

Which Ernest Hemingway novel is set in the Spanish Civil War?

11

What controversial novel about teenage violence appeared in 1962?

12

Whose only published novel is *To Kill a Mockingbird*?

ART & LITERATURE
MORE MODERN ART

1

Whose art features animals preserved in formaldehyde?

2

What nationality was the abstract painter Wassily Kandinsky?

3

Who created the giant topiary sculpture *Puppy* in 1992?

4

Which US artist is best known for his "color field" painting?

5

How old was Andy Warhol when he died?

6

Which ex-ad man is a leading patron of contemporary art?

7

What nationality was the Surrealist painter René Magritte?

8

Which artist was best known for his avant-garde photography?

9

Artist Georgia O'Keeffe famously painted what?

10

Henry Moore and David Hockney are both natives of which county?

11

Whaam! is a work by which Pop Artist?

12

Where in Spain is the Guggenheim Museum?

1

In the Beatrix Potter stories, what is Mr Jeremy Fisher?

2

Who wrote *The Iron Man*?

3

What animal is Baloo in *The Jungle Book*?

4

Who is the author/illustrator of *In the Night Kitchen*?

5

What is "It" in *Five Children and It*?

6

Who was the blind man in *Treasure Island*?

7

Which Anne Fine novel became the movie *Mrs Doubtfire*?

8

Whose first children's story was *Stuart Little*?

9

Which Roald Dahl character was named after a foot complaint?

10

In *The Water Babies*, what is Tom's job?

11

What are ordinary mortals called in the Harry Potter books?

12

What is the final book in the "His Dark Materials" trilogy?

1

Who wrote *The Turn of the Screw*?

2

What New York hotel was a famous residence for creative artists?

3

In which country was J R R Tolkien born?

4

Who is the author of the Waverley novels?

5

Who was *The New Yorker* cartoonist of *Men, Women and Dogs*?

6

What was the 18thC novelist Henry Fielding's "day job"?

7

Which American Civil War general wrote *Ben-Hur*?

8

Which 1971 novel by William Peter Blatty became a hit movie?

9

Which was the first novel published by Stephen King?

10

Who conducted the Owl and the Pussycat's wedding?

11

Casper Gutman is a villain in which private eye novel?

12

Who wrote *Tanglewood Tales for Girls and Boys*?

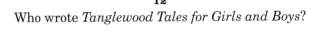

MOVIES & TELEVISION
MOVIE TITLES (1): ADD THE NUMBERS

1

. . . Angry Men

2

. . . Days of the Condor

3

Butterfield . . .

4

. . . Rode Together

5

. . . Rue Madeleine

6

. . . Paces to Baker Street

7

. . . Days to Noon

8

. . . and a Half Weeks

9

. . . in the Shade

10

. . . Degrees of Separation

11

The . . . Pennies

12

. . . Years in Sing Sing

MOVIES & TELEVISION
TV SITCOMS

1

What is the name of the butler in *The Fresh Prince of Bel Air*?

2

What is Dr Frasier Crane's middle name?

3

In what borough of New York is *Becker* set?

4

What headgear did Lt Colonel Blake in *M.A.S.H* usually wear?

5

What are the respective professions of Norm and Cliff in *Cheers*?

6

How many times did Ross in *Friends* get divorced?

7

Where is Master Sergeant Ernie Bilko based?

8

In *Bewitched*, who took over the role of Darrin from Dick York?

9

All in the Family was adapted from which UK TV series?

10

Name the character played by Christopher Lloyd in *Taxi*.

11

Who created *The Dick Van Dyke Show*?

12

Which chat-show host collects vintage cars and motorcycles?

MOVIES & TELEVISION
WHAT ARE THEIR "MOVIE STAR" NAMES?

1

Roy Scherer

2

John Charles Carter

3

Margarita Carmen Cansino

4

William Henry Pratt

5

Caryn Elaine Johnson

6

Issur Danielovich

7

Betty Perske

8

Alphonso Joseph d'Abruzzo

9

Krishna Bhanji

10

Frederick Austerlitz

11

Cherilyn Sarkisian

12

James Lablanche Stewart

1

Who plays Doc Holliday in *Gunfight at the OK Corral*?

2

In which Western is Gregory Peck a man of the sea?

3

Who directed *The Wild Bunch*?

4

In which movie is John Wayne The Ringo Kid?

5

Who are the musical duo in *Cat Ballou*?

6

Who starred in *The Man from Laramie*?

7

Brokeback Mountain is based on whose short story?

8

Ride the High Country is known by which other name?

9

Who plays Vin in *The Magnificent Seven*?

10

Who does Henry Fonda play in *My Darling Clementine*?

11

Who is the female attraction in *Once Upon a Time in the West*?

12

Who directed himself in *One Eyed Jacks*?

1

Who played Della Street in the original *Perry Mason* TV series?

2

What are the robots in *Blade Runner* called?

3

In which movie did Meryl Streep make her big screen debut?

4

On which day of the year did Dean Martin die?

5

In which year did *Saturday Night Live* first air?

6

Which movie ends with the line: "Nobody's perfect"?

7

Who played Hawkeye Pierce in the movie version of *M.A.S.H*?

8

Which two families share *Soap*?

9

What was James Dean's middle name?

10

Who is the most famous resident of Cabot Cove, Maine?

11

Who was first choice for the title role in *Shakespeare in Love*?

12

In which movie did Eminem make his movie debut?

MOVIES & TELEVISION
TV CRIMEBUSTERS

1

What are Starsky and Hutch's first names?

2

Who played private eye Mike Hammer in the 1980s series?

3

Which New York cop had a penchant for lollipops?

4

Name the police detective in pursuit of *The Fugitive*.

5

What was the name of the first desk sergeant in *Hill Street Blues*?

6

Who played the title role in the 1950s series *Peter Gunn*?

7

Which city was private eye Dan Tanna's beat?

8

Who was perfect casting for the overweight detective Frank Cannon?

9

Who did Jimmy Smits replace in *NYPD Blue*?

10

Which fraternal movie directors produce the TV series *Numb3rs*?

11

Who first played Dr Amanda Bentley in *Diagnosis Murder*?

12

What is private eye Jim Rockford's father's given name?

MOVIES & TELEVISION
FESTIVALS AND AWARDS

1

What do the initials BAFTA stand for?

2

In which year were the Oscars first presented?

3

Which John Wayne movie won him his only Oscar?

4

Who was the first African American actress to win an Oscar?

5

What is the major prize at the Venice Film Festival?

6

Who won both a BAFTA and an Oscar for "Best Actor" in 2008?

7

Who refused his Oscar for "Best Actor" in 1970?

8

Julia Roberts won an Oscar in 2001 for which film?

9

For which movie did Jack Nicholson receive his second Oscar?

10

Who was the first Englishman to win an Oscar?

11

Who founded the Sundance Movie Festival?

12

Which British movie won nine Oscars in 1997?

MOVIES & TELEVISION
CRIME MOVIES

1

Who plays the title role in *Klute*?

2

Who directed *American Gangster*?

3

What movie paired Robert de Niro and Al Pacino for the first time?

4

In what movie is a cop played by Andy Garcia decapitated?

5

Who loses her head in *Seven*?

6

Who plays the bounty hunter in *No Country for Old Men*?

7

In which movie does Albert Finney play an aspiring private eye?

8

Which Great Train Robber did Phil Collins play?

9

To what does private eye Micky Rourke descend to in *Angel Heart*?

10

In which movie is Elliott Gould private eye Philip Marlowe?

11

Name the private detective played by Jack Nicholson in *Chinatown*.

12

In which movie did Tony Curtis play Albert DeSalvo?

1

Which comedy duo sang "On The Trail Of The Lonesome Pine"?

2

In *Roseanne*, what is the title character's full name?

3

Who made their movie debut in the 1949 movie *My Friend Irma*?

4

Who plays Larry David's wife in *Curb Your Enthusiasm*?

5

In which movie is Steve Martin a character called Dr Hfuhruhurr?

6

What do Larry, Curly, and Mo add up to?

7

In which TV show was "No soup for you!" a catchphrase?

8

Who is Danny DeVito's character in *Taxi*?

9

What was the sitcom *Ellen* originally called?

10

What was the last name of Benson the butler?

11

Bret McKenzie and Jemaine Clement star in which TV comedy series?

12

Whose jazz band makes an unlikely appearance in *Blazing Saddles*?

MOVIES & TELEVISION
MULTISCREEN (2)

1

Cheers' Sam Malone is a former pitcher for which baseball team?

2

Name the movie-making Coen Brothers.

3

Who played C J Cregg in *The West Wing*?

4

Which Harry Potter movie was released in 2007?

5

Which organization presents the Golden Globe Awards?

6

Film actor Edward Norton is fluent in which foreign language?

7

What do the initials CBS stand for?

8

Which New Zealand director made *Heavenly Bodies*?

9

What is the name of the UK version of *Dancing With The Stars*?

10

Which movie director shares the name of a famous explorer?

11

What was *The Ed Sullivan Show* originally called?

12

Which four Oscar-winning Aussies appeared on postage stamps?

1

Which was the first James Bond movie?

2

Who sang "Die Another Day" in the movie of that name?

3

Who played Bond the most times, Sean Connery or Roger Moore?

4

Who was 007 in *Licence to Kill*?

5

Who was 006 in *GoldenEye*?

6

What nationality is one-time Bond George Lazenby?

7

What is the most destructive thing about Oddjob?

8

What did Donald Pleasence, Telly Savalas, and Charles Gray share?

9

In which Bond movie did Rowan Atkinson make his big screen debut?

10

Which actor first played "Q"?

11

Who played "Sir James Bond" in the 1967 version of *Casino Royale*?

12

Who was younger on Bond debut, Daniel Craig or Sean Connery?

1

Who plays Dr Frank N Furter in *The Rocky Horror Picture Show*?

2

What are the rival gangs in *West Side Story*?

3

High Society is a musical remake of which movie?

4

Who plays Mrs Banks in *Mary Poppins*?

5

Who wrote the music for *Sweet Charity*?

6

The musical *Guys and Dolls* is based on whose stories?

7

What was Fred Astaire and Ginger Rogers' last movie together?

8

Who plays Juan Perón in the movie of *Evita*?

9

Which British director won an Oscar for *Oliver!*?

10

In which movie is the musical number "Make 'Em Laugh"?

11

Who was originally cast as the male lead in *Easter Parade*?

12

Who plays Roxie Hart's husband in the movie *Chicago*?

1

Shirley Temple Black became US ambassador to which two countries?

2

Before she became famous, which actress worked in an ice-cream shop?

3

Who was a qualified hair stylist before his career in the movies?

4

Who worked as a street mime before he got into acting?

5

Which rugged actor and director started out as a pool boy?

6

Which Greek actress became her country's Minister of Arts?

7

Which Hollywood icon became a director of Fabergé?

8

Which former teenage star became a cocktail waitress?

9

What further career did Gina Lollobrigida successfully take up?

10

Which 1940s Hollywood star became a Manhattan barmaid?

11

Who founded the World Adoption International Fund?

12

Who launched his own salad dressing?

MOVIES & TELEVISION
MOVIE TITLES (2): ADD THE PLACE NAMES

1

Sleepless in . . .

2

. . . Danny Rose

3

North to . . .

4

Letters from . . .

5

Fair Wind to . . .

6

The Thief of . . .

7

Next Stop . . . Village

8

The Spirit of . . .

9

Won Ton Ton, the Dog Who Saved . . .

10

The . . . Story

11

A Night in . . .

12

Thirty Seconds over . . .

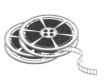

1

What type of gun does "Dirty Harry" Callahan carry?

2

In which musical Western does Clint Eastwood co-star?

3

What is the name of Eastwood's character in *Unforgiven*?

4

What was Clint Eastwood's first movie as director?

5

In which movie does Eastwood play a professional thief?

6

In *White Hunter, Black Heart*, who is Eastwood's role based on?

7

Eastwood shot to fame playing who in the TV series *Rawhide*?

8

What political office did Clint Eastwood take on in 1986?

9

In *Space Cowboys*, who played Eastwood's three fellow astronauts?

10

In which film does Eastwood play someone called Walt Kowalski?

11

Who plays Lone Watie in *The Outlaw Josey Wales*?

12

Which three play the "Good", the "Bad," and the "Ugly"?

MOVIES & TELEVISION
MULTISCREEN (3)

1

Nicole Kidman won an Oscar for her portrayal of whom in *The Hours*?

2

Which planet was Mork from?

3

Cheers' Sam Malone is a former pitcher for which baseball team?

4

In which movie did Flubber make its first appearance?

5

Who wrote a book about her pet chipmunk called *Nibbles and Me*?

6

Who is Fred Flintstone's best friend?

7

Who plays Prince Philip in *The Queen*?

8

What was John Wayne's real name?

9

Who are the boy-band cherubs in *Night at the Museum 2*?

10

What is Julie Walter's role in the Harry Potter movies?

11

Which screen comic co-founded United Artists in 1919?

12

Who played Major Winters in *Band of Brothers*?

MOVIES & TELEVISION
ANIMALS ON SCREEN

1

Who does Marcel the monkey belong to?

2

What kind of cat does Blofeld in the Bond movies have?

3

What was the name of Roy Rogers' horse?

4

What is the name of Dorothy's dog in *The Wizard of Oz*?

5

How many spots has Pongo in *101 Dalmations*?

6

What is Elizabeth Taylor's horse is *National Velvet* called?

7

How was a Hollywood male collie called Pal better known?

8

Who leapt to fame in the movie *Free Willy*?

9

Which father and son played Eddie in *Frasier*?

10

Which doggy actor played Old Yeller in the movie of the same name?

11

What canine breed was Rin Tin Tin?

12

Who was Clint Eastwood's simian pal in *Every Which Way But Loose*?

MOVIES & TELEVISION
TV DRAMA

1

For which advertising agency does Don Draper work?

2

What role did Alexis Smith play in *Dallas*?

3

In *The West Wing*, what is the character John Hoynes?

4

Who wrote the award-winning drama *Angels in America*?

5

To what painkiller is Dr Gregory House addicted?

6

In the 1980s series *Hotel*, what was the name of the hotel?

7

Which Italian movie actress turned up in *Falcon Crest*?

8

Name the theme song from *The Sopranos*?

9

What is the principal movie location for *Lost*?

10

In *24*, what is the name of Jack Bauer's brother?

11

Who played Caress Morell in *Dynasty*?

12

Which character did Alec Baldwin play in *Knots Landing*?

MOVIES & TELEVISION
FAMILY CONNECTIONS

1

Who is Melanie Griffith's actress mother?

2

How were Rita Hayworth and Ginger Rogers related?

3

Who is the older Bridges brother, Beau or Jeff?

4

Who was Dudley Moore's first wife?

5

Who was Anne Baxter's famous grandfather?

6

Who was Angelina Jolie's first husband?

7

Michael Sheen's father was a professional lookalike of whom?

8

Who was Mia Farrow's movie star mother?

9

Joely Richardson's grandfather was which star of stage and screen?

10

Which two granddaughters of Ernest Hemingway made it into movies?

11

Who is writer Sharman Macdonald's more famous daughter?

12

Dana Andrews was the brother of which fellow Hollywood star?

1

"Book 'em, Danno!"

2

"Everybody wants to get into the act."

3

"D'oh!"

4

"Here's Johnny!"

5

"Sock it to me."

6

"Who loves ya, Baby?"

7

"Now cut that out!"

8

"This is the city . . ."

9

"Yabba dabba do."

10

"Just one more thing . . ."

11

"Say goodnight, Gracie."

12

"And that's the way it is."

1

On whose short story is *The Birds* based?

2

Who plays the private investigator in *Psycho*?

3

Which husband and wife appeared in *Witness for the Prosecution*?

4

Which one of his movies did Hitchcock remake in 1956?

5

In *Rear Window,* James Stewart's character does what for a living?

6

Who created the dream sequence in the movie *Spellbound*?

7

Which Hitchcock movie takes place in Australia?

8

Who played Richard Hannay in *The 39 Steps*?

9

What most concerns Charters and Caldicott in *The Lady Vanishes*?

10

In *Torn Curtain*, Hitchcock makes a brief appearance holding what?

11

Where does the climax to *North by Northwest* take place?

12

What was Hitchcock's last movie?

1

In which gangster movie did Pierce Brosnan make his screen debut?

2

Which of the Hollywood Ten wrote the screenplay for *Exodus*?

3

Which husband and wife were in the 1994 remake of *The Getaway*?

4

Who directed *The Curious Case of Benjamin Button*?

5

Who is the resident scientist on *The Muppet Show*?

6

Whose eight minutes on screen were enough for an Oscar in 1998?

7

Which 007 once posed nude for an art class?

8

Which British sitcom was remade as *Three's Company*?

9

Which fish had a starring role in a 1988 hit movie?

10

What is the top prize at the Cannes Film Festival?

11

In which country was Audrey Hepburn born?

12

Who plays Aragorn in *The Lord of the Rings*?

GEOGRAPHY
GLOBETROTTING (1)

1

What is Switzerland's largest city?

2

San José is the capital of which country?

3

What is fine sediment deposited by a river called?

4

Which country was once known as Cathay?

5

What is the national language of Pakistan?

6

Panama hats originated in which country?

7

To which country do the Azores belong?

8

Which sea is at the northern end of the Suez Canal?

9

Who is Bolivia named after?

10

Patagonia is a region of which country?

11

On what river does St Petersburg stand?

12

What is the port of Athens?

GEOGRAPHY
ROLLING RIVERS

1

Which river is longer, Chang or Yellow?

2

Into which sea does the Mekong river flow?

3

The Kariba Dam is on which African river?

4

On which river does Munich stand?

5

What is France's longest river?

6

The Vistula flows through which capital city?

7

Into which sea does the River Jordan flow?

8

In which country is the source of the White Nile?

9

Which river flows from the Himalayas to the Bay of Bengal?

10

Hanoi is located on the right bank of which river?

11

What is the longest river in Canada?

12

On which river is Perth, Australia?

GEOGRAPHY
MOUNTAINS HIGH

48

1

Which mountain range divides France and Spain?

2

Mt Elbert is which US mountain range's highest peak?

3

What is the highest mountain in Africa?

4

In which country are the Southern Alps?

5

What is Antarctica's highest mountain?

6

In which country are the Dolomites?

7

What is the highest mountain in Portugal?

8

What is the highest mountain in Europe?

9

What is the world's longest mountain range?

10

Mt Everest stands in which two countries?

11

Which is the highest peak in the Appalachians?

12

In which country is The Great Dividing Range?

1
Sri Lanka

2
Malawi

3
Belize

4
Bangladesh

5
Thailand

6
Iran

7
Democratic Republic of the Congo

8
Mexico

9
Ghana

10
Kiribati

11
Ethiopia

12
Mali

GEOGRAPHY
GLOBETROTTING (2)

1

Which state is known as the Diamond State?

2

Which country surrounds San Marino?

3

What is the name of the world's largest gulf?

4

What is the official language of the Ivory Coast?

5

What is the capital of Taiwan?

6

Which country has the shortest coastline in the world?

7

In which Spanish city is the Alhambra palace?

8

Which is farther north, Adelaide or Canberra?

9

What is Japan's highest peak?

10

The Victoria Falls are on which African river?

11

Which state borders just one other state?

12

Malta comprises what three inhabited islands?

GEOGRAPHY
WAVING THE FLAG

1

Which country's flag features a maple leaf?

2

What are the colors of the Polish flag?

3

What do the stripes on the American flag represent?

4

How many stars are there on the Chinese national flag?

5

Does the French tricolore have vertical or horizontal stripes?

6

What is the largest star on the Australian flag called?

7

What colors are the German flag, in descending order?

8

Which two symbols are featured on Turkey's national flag?

9

Which country's flag is a solid red circle on a white background?

10

Which UK island's flag features three conjoined legs?

11

What are the colors of the Italian flag, left to right?

12

How many stars are on the flag of the European Union?

GEOGRAPHY
ISLANDS OF THE SEA

1

To which country do the Faroe Islands belong?

2

Which country includes the Isle of Tiree?

3

On which Canadian island is the city of Victoria?

4

Which is New Zealand's larger island, North or South?

5

Kos and Symi are in which group of Greek islands?

6

In which ocean are the Heard and McDonald islands?

7

What is the world's smallest island nation?

8

How many major islands make up the Azores?

9

What is the largest island in Asia?

10

Rarotonga is the capital of which islands?

11

Robinson Crusoe Island lies off the coast of which country?

12

On which island is Tokyo situated?

GEOGRAPHY
LAKES

1

In which country is Lake Garda?

2

Which is the smallest of the Five Great Lakes?

3

Which two South American countries border Lake Titicaca?

4

Which is the world's deepest lake?

5

In which US state is Lake Okeechobee?

6

On which New Zealand island is Lake Taupo?

7

Which country has the minority share of Lake Geneva?

8

In which mountain range is Lake Tahoe situated?

9

Which four states border Lake Erie?

10

What is the world's largest lake?

11

In which region of Canada is Great Bear Lake?

12

What lake is the lowest point in Australia?

1

Where in India is the Taj Mahal?

2

Where will you find the ancient ruins of Carthage?

3

What is the name of the most famous bridge in Florence?

4

In which country are the Shakta Pantjukhina caves?

5

Which four presidents can be seen on Mount Rushmore?

6

Which New Zealand city is known for its geothermal activity?

7

In which country is The Giant's Causeway?

8

Uluru is the aboriginal name for what?

9

Where in Egypt is the Great Pyramid?

10

The Reichenbach Falls are in which country?

11

In which famous square is St Basil's Cathedral?

12

In which country is Machu Picchu?

GEOGRAPHY
GLOBETROTTING (3)

1

What is the Israeli parliament called?

2

What is the second longest river in the world?

3

What is the capital of Estonia?

4

In which South American country is Lake Maracaibo?

5

What three countries border Luxembourg?

6

In which national park is the geyser "Old Faithful"?

7

What is the world's longest canal?

8

Which major river has its source in the Black Forest?

9

Which is farthest south Madrid or Washington DC?

10

New Caledonia is an overseas territory of which European country?

11

What mountain range broadly separates Europe from Asia?

12

Where are the Spanish Steps?

1

What does occidental mean?

2

Which is longer, a nautical mile or a land mile?

3

In which hemisphere is the Tropic of Cancer?

4

What is the meeting of two rivers called?

5

What is measured on the Richter Scale?

6

What is a large, flat-topped landform with steep rocky walls?

7

What is a cataract?

8

What is a group of islands called?

9

What word describes a shallow lake of salt water?

10

What is chorology?

11

What is molten rock below the earth's crust called?

12

What is a wadi?

GEOGRAPHY
SEAS AND OCEANS

1

Which ocean covers more than a third of the earth's surface?

2

The Bass Strait separates which two areas of land?

3

Where are the highest tides in the world recorded?

4

Which sea has the highest concentration of salt?

5

What is the world's smallest ocean?

6

What links the Mediterranean Sea to the Atlantic Ocean?

7

Which sea is located north of Norway and Russia?

8

In which sea is the Great Barrier Reef?

9

Which two gulfs are linked by the Strait of Hormuz?

10

Which ocean has the deepest point?

11

Which strait connects the Pacific and Atlantic oceans?

12

Which sea lies between Sardinia and mainland Italy?

GEOGRAPHY
DESERT LANDSCAPES

1

What is the driest inhabited continent on Earth?

2

What mountain range is to the north of the Sahara?

3

By which other name is the Great Indian Desert known?

4

What is the world's largest desert?

5

Which two countries share the Gobi Desert?

6

In what state is the Colorado Desert?

7

What percentage of Egypt is desert?

8

The Kalahari Desert spans which two African countries?

9

Which desert contains the driest place on Earth?

10

In which Australian state is the Great Sandy Desert?

11

In which desert will you find the Joshua tree?

12

Which Chinese desert is known as the "Sea of Death"?

1

What became the new capital of Germany in 1999?

2

By what name was Harare previously known?

3

What is the capital of Florida?

4

Bratislava is the capital of which European country?

5

How is Te Whanganui-a-Tara better known?

6

What is the capital of Paraguay?

7

What is the most northerly capital in the world?

8

What is the provincial capital of Saskatchewan in Canada?

9

North Dakota's capital is the name of which German statesman?

10

Which capital city is on the River Liffey?

11

What is the capital of Rwanda?

12

What is the highest capital city in the world?

GEOGRAPHY
GLOBETROTTING (4)

1

Which is the largest Central American republic?

2

What is New England's only national park?

3

What is the capital of Ecuador?

4

Which two countries are separated by the Kattegat?

5

What is the largest city in the Crimea?

6

What state is nicknamed the "Beaver State"?

7

What are the Moluccan Islands also known as?

8

Which country has the largest gold reserves?

9

Scapa Flow is in which group of islands?

10

What is the port of Perth in Western Australia?

11

The porcelain-making town of Meissen stands on which river?

12

Which is Europe's highest capital city?

GEOGRAPHY
NAME THEIR CURRENCY

1

South Africa

2

Vietnam

3

Israel

4

Cuba

5

Egypt

6

China

7

Russia

8

South Korea

9

Switzerland

10

Brazil

11

Denmark

12

Mongolia

GEOGRAPHY
AIRPORTS OF THE WORLD

1

What is Chicago's major airport?

2

Schiphol is which city's airport?

3

By what name was New York's JFK airport previously known?

4

Prestwick airport is near to which Scottish city?

5

Which city's airport is named Leonardo da Vinci?

6

What is the name of Hong Kong's international airport?

7

Which city's airport was previously called Kingsford-Smith?

8

What is the name of London's largest airport?

9

After which famous explorer is Venice's airport named?

10

Chhatrapati Shivaji airport serves which Indian city?

11

Which Canadian airport is named after a former prime minister?

12

Where is Narita International Airport?

1

Beijing

2

Gdańsk

3

Ho Chi Minh City

4

New York

5

Dhaka

6

Oslo

7

Maputo

8

Istanbul

9

Nizhny Novgorod

10

Tokyo

11

Mumbai

12

Kinshasa

1

Which state is known as the "Heart of Dixie"?

2

In which state is located the lowest point in the US?

3

What is America's second smallest state?

4

Which state is closest to Bermuda?

5

Helena is the capital city of which state?

6

In which state is the source of the Mississippi River?

7

Which state is the farthest west?

8

Which state shares its northern border with South Dakota?

9

In which state is the volcanic Mount St Helens?

10

Which is the only state to share its name with its capital city?

11

Which state's motto is "She Flies With Her Own Wings"?

12

The "Show Me State" is the nickname of which state?

GEOGRAPHY
GLOBETROTTING (5)

1

Which city is served by George Bush Intercontinental airport?

2

How is the Greek island of Kerkyra better known?

3

In which other country does London stand on the River Thames?

4

What was Boston's original name?

5

What two rivers merge to become the Shatt-al-Arab?

6

On how many hills is Rome built?

7

Which country's flag is solid green?

8

In which country is Transylvania?

9

What is the largest island in the Philippines?

10

What is Canada's highest mountain?

11

What is the largest city within the Arctic Circle?

12

Where is Timbuktu?

HISTORY
WAR AND PEACE

66

1

How many Crusades were there?

2

Which war ended with the Treaty of Panmunjom?

3

In which battle did the Sioux defeat General Custer?

4

Who was The War of Jenkin's Ear between?

5

In which war was the Battle of Brandywine Creek?

6

Who was defeated at Dien Bien Phu in 1954?

7

Who was Russia at war with in 1904-05?

8

What war came to an end in August 1988?

9

How long did the Hundred Years War last?

10

In which year was the Treaty of Versailles?

11

What was the shelling of Fort Sumter the start of?

12

Who was the Peloponnesian War between?

1

Whose assassination in Sarajevo in 1914 led to the war?

2

How were French soldiers transported to the battle of the Marne?

3

In which country was the battle of Ypres fought?

4

What war service did Ernest Hemingway undertake?

5

What armored vehicle made its first appearance during the war?

6

Who wrote the poem "Suicide in the Trenches"?

7

Which two countries commemorate ANZAC Day?

8

To which country did Kaiser Wilhelm II flee in 1918?

9

During which battle was poison gas first used?

10

Who commanded the US Expeditionary Force?

11

Who became known as the "Butcher of the Somme"?

12

Who were known as the "Old Contemptibles"?

HISTORY
WHO SAID THAT?

68

1

"History is bunk."

2

"All I know is that I am not a Marxist."

3

"The one duty we owe to history is to rewrite it."

4

"Is Paris burning?"

5

"France has lost the battle but she has not lost the war."

6

"Your president is no crook."

7

"The ballot is stronger than the bullet."

8

"If you want a friend in Washington, get a dog."

9

"Power corrupts, but lack of power corrupts absolutely."

10

"I will make you shorter by a head."

11

"How can a president not be an actor?"

12

"If we lose this war, I'll start another in my wife's name."

HISTORY
PAST TIMES (1)

1

Which country became part of Great Britain in 1801?

2

What opened in New York on October 27 1904?

3

What was the world's first skyscraper?

4

Where did Alexander the Great die?

5

Which was the first republic in Western Europe?

6

Which civilization built Machu Picchu?

7

Who made famous the phrase "The Iron Curtain"?

8

For how long was John Paul I the Pope?

9

How did Gestapo chief Heinrich Himmler die?

10

For how many years did Queen Victoria reign?

11

What institution did George Williams found in London in 1844?

12

In which year did the Vietnam War end?

1

In which year did the Russian Revolution begin?

2

When was NATO founded?

3

When was the Great Fire of London?

4

In which year did Fidel Castro come to power in Cuba?

5

In which year did Saddam Hussein become president of Iraq?

6

When was the "Six Day" Arab-Israeli war?

7

What year was the Lockerbie air disaster?

8

When did the Berlin Wall come down?

9

When was the "Boston Tea Party" protest?

10

When was Nelson Mandela released from prison?

11

In which year was October 19 "Black Monday"?

12

In which year was Mahatma Gandhi assassinated?

1

Queen Margrethe II is the reigning monarch of which country?

2

Who was the last czar of Russia?

3

Who was the Dutch queen who died in 2004?

4

Which French king was guillotined in 1793?

5

How many of Henry VIII's six wives were beheaded?

6

Who was the last king of Italy?

7

Of which country was King Zog the ruler?

8

What nationality was French queen Marie Antoinette?

9

Who became emperor of France in 1852?

10

Which Egyptian king abdicated in 1952?

11

Who became Saudi Arabia's first king in 1932?

12

Which Japanese ruler died in 1989?

HISTORY
THE CIVIL WAR

1

Who was vice president of the Confederate States?

2

Which siege ended on July 4, 1863?

3

The battle of Shiloh was fought alongside which major river?

4

Which Confederate general wore a red-lined cape and yellow sash?

5

Who commanded the Union army at Gettysburg?

6

Who was Secretary of State throughout the Lincoln presidency?

7

Which two Confederate generals share the same last name?

8

Name the Union ship that defeated the icon-clad *Merrimack*.

9

What was the notorious prisoner-of-war camp in Georgia?

10

What was General Sherman's middle name?

11

Which Union general later wrote the classic novel *Ben-Hur*?

12

Whose photographs memorably recorded the entire war?

73

1

When was the Bay of Pigs invasion of Cuba?

2

Who was the first American to orbit the earth?

3

Whose report on the death of President Kennedy came out in 1964?

4

Who was the American U2 pilot captured by the Russians?

5

Whose book *Silent Spring* launched the environmental movement?

6

Which African American leader was assassinated in 1965?

7

Who succeeded Pope John XXIII in 1963?

8

Which writing instrument was launched in Japan in 1960?

9

What was the 1968 revolution in Czechoslovakia called?

10

Who became Israel's first female prime minister in 1969?

11

Which major new passenger aircraft was test-flown in 1969?

12

In which country was Che Guevara killed in 1967?

1

Vladimir Illyich Ulyanov

2

Manfred von Richthofen

3

Malcolm Little

4

Dolores Ibarruri

5

Siddhartha Gautama

6

Thomas Edward Lawrence

7

Agnes Gonxha Bojaxhiu

8

Rodrigo Diaz de Vivar

9

Leslie King

10

Lev Davidovitch Bronstein

11

Saloth Sar

12

Josip Broz

HISTORY
PAST TIMES (2)

1

In which year did the New York City Subway open?

2

Who wrote *The Rights of Man*?

3

Who was the unfortunate captain of HMS *Bounty*?

4

Who was the Apache chief who died in 1909?

5

Who succeeded his mother as prime minister of India?

6

In which year did Prohibition end?

7

Who was the first woman to fly the Atlantic solo?

8

Who founded the Christian Science movement?

9

Which country did Russia invade in 1956?

10

Who was the notorious boss of New York's Tammany Hall?

11

Which sheriff killed Billy the Kid?

12

What nationality was the spy Mata Hari?

1

Which country had a revolution in 1789?

2

Which country was renamed the Khmer Republic in 1970?

3

Which country joined the European Community in 1981?

4

Which country tried to invade England in 1588?

5

Which country ended its civil war in 1994?

6

Which country invaded France in 1870?

7

Which country split into two in 1993?

8

Which country became whole again in 1990?

9

Which country was ceded to Russia in 1809?

10

Which country became Sri Lanka in 1972?

11

Which country beheaded its monarch in 1649?

12

Which country finally became independent from China in 939?

HISTORY
PAST TIMES (3)

1

Who was Blackbeard the pirate?

2

Who was the first UN Secretary General?

3

Who made his scientific voyages on the ship *HMS Beagle*?

4

What did the US purchase from Russia in 1867?

5

Who was the only English pope to date?

6

"Traveller" was which Civil War general's horse?

7

Which is the world's oldest parliament?

8

In which century was the Taj Mahal built?

9

Where in 1914 was the world's first traffic light installed?

10

Who was Czar Nicholas II's youngest daughter?

11

What was Van Diemen's Land later renamed?

12

In which year were the New York Draft Riots?

1

Which Marxist became president of Chile in 1970?

2

What product disappeared from American television in 1971?

3

Who in 1972 became the first president to visit China?

4

What honor was bestowed on Charlie Chaplin in 1975?

5

Which woman received the 1979 Nobel Peace Prize?

6

Which vice-president was forced to resign in 1973?

7

How old was Bill Gates when he co-founded Microsoft in 1975?

8

In which year was the Yom Kippur War?

9

Which heiress was kidnapped by the Symbionese Liberation Army?

10

Who became president of Uganda in 1971?

11

Who was elected governor of California in 1974?

12

Who was the instigator of the 1978 Jonestown massacre?

1

In which year was the Panama Canal opened?

2

When was the first supersonic flight?

3

In which year was the My Lai massacre?

4

When was the Battle of the Somme?

5

When was Saddam Hussein captured?

6

In which year was Abraham Lincoln assassinated?

7

When was the partitioning of India and Pakistan?

8

When did the Californian Gold Rush begin?

9

In which year did Queen Victoria come to the throne?

10

In which year was the Cuban missile crisis?

11

In which year was Coca Cola invented?

12

When was the Charge of the Light Brigade?

1

Which two great military adversaries were born in 1769?

2

Hannibal led which army across the Alps?

3

Which French general served with Washington at Valley Forge?

4

Who conquered the Aztecs in 1521?

5

Who was known as "Stormin' Norman"?

6

Which German field marshal became his country's president in 1925?

7

Who was the chivalrous Muslim leader who fought the Crusaders?

8

Which Civil War general became 18th president of the United States?

9

Who became the United States first Fleet Admiral in 1944?

10

Who was the victorious Red Army commander at Stalingrad?

11

Who was the first Allied general to land in France on D-Day?

12

Who captured Quebec in 1759 and died in the process?

1

What was Richard Nixon's middle name?

2

Which president was a professional mining engineer?

3

Which president was assassinated in 1881?

4

Who was Thomas Jefferson's second vice president?

5

Who was the 12th president?

6

Who was the first unmarried president?

7

Who was the first president to visit Europe while in office?

8

Which president died of a cold caught on Inauguration Day?

9

Which president was nicknamed "Old Hickory"?

10

Which president was only 5 feet, 6 inches tall?

11

Which two former presidents died on the same day?

12

Who did Abraham Lincoln defeat in the 1864 election?

1

In which ship did Francis Drake circumnavigate the world?

2

Who was the first American woman to travel in space?

3

Which explorer was killed in the Philippines in 1521?

4

Who led the first crossing of Antarctica in 1958?

5

Which country did Robert Burke and William Wills explore?

6

Who opened the first sea route to India?

7

In which country was the explorer H M Stanley born?

8

Which European explorer served the Mongol emperor Kublai Khan?

9

What was third time lucky for Ranulph Fiennes in 2009?

10

Which British explorer translated the *Kama Sutra*?

11

Which African river did Mungo Park chart?

12

Who was America named after?

HISTORY
NICKNAMES

1

Who was the "Iron Duke"?

2

Who was referred to as the "Teflon President"?

3

Who was known as the "Scourge of God"?

4

Who was "Papa Doc"?

5

Who was the "Little Corporal"?

6

Which general was known as the "Desert Fox"?

7

Who was known as the "The Iron Lady"?

8

Who was called "Old Blood and Guts" by his troops?

9

Who was known as "Sarko"?

10

Who was the "Iron Chancellor"?

11

Who was the "Sun King"?

12

Who was called the "Pineapple Face"?

1

What was the name of the first US space shuttle?

2

Which London embassy did terrorists seize in 1980?

3

Who murdered John Lennon?

4

What did Australia celebrate in 1988?

5

What spilled 11 million gallons of oil in Alaska?

6

In what year was the Chernobyl nuclear disaster?

7

Who was the president of Austria with a Nazi past?

8

Who did George Bush Sr. defeat in the 1988 US election?

9

Which country did the US invade in 1983?

10

Who became French president in 1981?

11

Which world leader survived an assassination attempt in 1981?

12

Name the prime minister assassinated by Sikh extremists in 1984.

HISTORY
WORLD WAR II

85

1

What was Operation Barbarossa?

2

What was August 15, 1945?

3

Who succeeded Adolf Hitler as Nazi leader?

4

When was the Battle of the Coral Sea?

5

Who was the victorious general at the Battle of El Alamein?

6

Which Nazi flew to Scotland on a secret mission in 1941?

7

What was the Maquis?

8

Which two beaches were US invasion targets on D-Day?

9

On which US warship did the Japanese surrender?

10

Where in 1943 was the first meeting of the "Big Three" allies?

11

Who headed the Vichy government in France?

12

How old was Adolf Hitler when he died?

1

Whose face is said to have launched a thousand ships?

2

Which Roman emperor appointed his horse a consul?

3

Who founded the Persian Empire?

4

Which ancient city did Pericles rule?

5

Which Roman emperor built a wall between England and Scotland?

6

Who was the Roman god of fire?

7

In which country was Alexander the Great born?

8

Which gladiator led a slave revolt against the Romans?

9

How was the Greek philosopher Socrates made to take his own life?

10

Which Roman general wrote a history of the Gallic Wars?

11

Who was the Battle of Marathon in 490 BC between?

12

Who was considered the greatest of all Roman orators?

HISTORY
PAST TIMES (4)

1

Where was the World's Fair at which President McKinley was shot?

2

Whose mistress was Clara Petacci?

3

What did Howard Carter and Lord Carnarvon find in 1922?

4

Which was the last nation in the Americas to abolish slavery?

5

Who gave the world "sideburns"?

6

Nell Gwyn was the mistress of which English king?

7

In which century did the "Black Death" decimate Europe?

8

Who was the first man to fly solo around the world?

9

In which country was Ned Kelly a celebrated outlaw?

10

Who founded the Turkish Republic ?

11

Which Chinese dynasty came first, Ming or Qing?

12

What mail service was used during the 1870 siege of Paris?

1

Cream

2

The Beach Boys

3

The Supremes

4

The Drifters

5

The Temptations

6

The Four Seasons

7

The Four Tops

8

The Kinks

9

The Who

10

The Doors

11

Grateful Dead

12

Led Zeppelin

MUSIC
WHO DID THEY BECOME?

1

Georgios Kyriacos Panayiotou

2

Barry Pincus

3

Virginia Petterson Hensley

4

Elias Bates

5

Cordoza Calvin Broadus Jr

6

Yvette Stevens

7

Annie Mae Bullock

8

Marvin Lee Aday

9

David Robert Hayward-Jones

10

Steven Demetre Georgiou

11

The Paramounts

12

Israel Baline

1

Who were John, Paul and George before The Beatles?

2

Which major record company rejected The Beatles in 1962?

3

For whom did Paul McCartney write "Hey Jude"?

4

Which two Beatles are left-handed?

5

Which Beatle sang backing vocals on Donovan's "Mellow Yellow"?

6

With which Beatles' song did The Overlanders reach No 1 in 1966?

7

What was the name of John Lennon's cat?

8

Who parodied the lyrics of "A Hard Day's Night" as Richard III?

9

"Baby You're A Rich Man" is dedicated to whom?

10

Bernard Webb was the pseudonym of which Beatle?

11

The Beatles made their first live US performance on what TV show?

12

What was The Beatles' last US No 1?

MUSIC
WHICH POP GROUPS ARE THESE?

1

Fayette Pinkney, Sheila Ferguson, and Valerie Holiday.

2

Al Alberts, Dave Mahoney, Lou Silvestri, and Rosario Vaccaro.

3

Veronica Bennett, Estelle Bennett, and Nedra Talley.

4

Annie Lennox and Dave Stewart.

5

Levi Stubbs, Lawrence Payton, Abdul Fakir, and Renaldo Benson.

6

Eric Clapton, Jack Bruce, and Ginger Baker.

7

Neil Tennant and Chris Lowe.

8

Florence Ballard, Mary Wilson, Diana Ross, and Betty McGlown.

9

Joe Perry, Tom Hamilton, Steven Tyler, Joey Kramer, and Brad Whitford.

10

Bill Berry, Peter Buck, Mike Mills, and Michael Stipe.

11

Jimmy Page, Robert Plant, John Paul Jones, and John Bonham.

12

Peter Yarrow, Noel "Paul" Stookey, and Mary Travers.

1

What was B Bumble and the Stingers' 1962 hit?

2

What was the Mamas and the Papas only No 1 hit in the US?

3

Who is the oldest of the Everly Brothers, Don or Phil?

4

Who sang about the Texan town of Galveston?

5

Name the Rolling Stones' first US No 1 in 1965?

6

In which year did Elvis Presley get married?

7

Whose 1961 No 1 hit was "Take Good Care Of My Baby"?

8

In 1968, who covered Tony Bennett's hit "For Once In My Life"?

9

Who spent a good seven minutes in "MacArthur Park" in 1968?

10

Which Beach Boy was acquitted of draft evasion in 1967?

11

Which 60s group was made up of two pairs of sisters?

12

In 1966, which American father and daughter each had a UK No 1?

1

Who made the most of his 1959 deck of cards?

2

What is Paul McCartney's first name?

3

Who did David Essex play on stage in *Evita*?

4

How many were there originally in the Spice Girls?

5

What is the name of Russia's foremost ballet company?

6

Whose album "Bookends" was a UK and US No 1?

7

What did Stevie Wonder lose after a car crash in 1973?

8

Which of the Eurythmics once worked in a fish factory?

9

Who was the first African American soloist to sing at the New York Met?

10

Which rock star once worked as a gravedigger?

11

Who had a hit in 1972 with "Puppy Love"?

12

Which singer is known as "The Queen of Soul"?

1

What was Rodgers and Hammerstein's last musical together?

2

For which 1960s musical did Richard Kiley win a Tony award?

3

Whose poems inspired the musical *Cats*?

4

In which musical did Gene Kelly first star on Broadway?

5

Who played the title role in the original production of *Barnum*?

6

What song from *Kismet* became an international hit?

7

Who recreated his Broadway role in the movie of *Sweet Charity*?

8

Who wrote the music and lyrics for *Sweeney Todd*?

9

From which hit musical comes "Music Of The Night"?

10

Which Russian composer's music was adapted for *Kismet*?

11

"I Hope I Get It" is the opening number from which show?

12

Which Broadway musical has a "Fugue for Tinhorns"?

95

MUSIC
COLOR THESE SONGS

1

"The . . . Rose Of Texas"

2

"Paint It . . ."

3

"Shades Of . . ."

4

"Mood . . ."

5

" . . . Ribbons"

6

"Lily The . . ."

7

"Mellow . . ."

8

". . . Rain"

9

". . . Shirt"

10

"My Love Is . . ."

11

"Symphony In . . ."

12

"Fields Of . . ."

MUSIC
POP GOES THE 70s

1

Who was Sid Vicious's girlfriend?

2

Which UK group had a hit with "Good Morning Judge"?

3

In 1972 the Partridge Family covered which Neil Sedaka hit?

4

Which 1973 teen idol was a "Daydreamer"?

5

How old was Jimi Hendrix when he died in 1970?

6

What was Michael Jackson's first solo record?

7

"Sheena Is A Punk Rocker" was a hit for whom?

8

The Eagles was originally the backing group for which singer?

9

Who sang about "Puppy Love" in 1972?

10

In what year did Elvis Presley die?

11

How many people were in The Village People?

12

Who is Carly Simon's 1972 hit "You're So Vain" supposedly about?

1

Which group backed Buddy Holly?

2

What is Ozzy Osbourne's real name?

3

What was the last album The Beatles recorded?

4

Where is the home of the world-famous Concertgebouw Orchestra?

5

Who sings the title song for *High Noon* on the soundtrack?

6

Whose song-writing partner was Gerry Goffin?

7

What instrument did Glenn Miller play?

8

Whose follies went from Broadway to Hollywood?

9

Which movie featured the single "Vogue" by Madonna?

10

Which film won Oscars in 2009 for best original score and song?

11

What was John Lennon's middle name?

12

Who wrote the words, Gilbert or Sullivan?

MUSIC
ALL THAT JAZZ

1

Which legendary jazz guitarist was a gypsy?

2

What instrument did Bix Beiderbecke play?

3

Which father of jazz was always "Papa Joe" to Louis Armstrong?

4

Which big-band leader disappeared on a flight to France in 1944?

5

Who was "Empress of the Blues"?

6

"Pops" was one of his nicknames—what was the other?

7

Who was the "King of Swing"?

8

Which iconic jazz singer was a former prostitute?

9

Who are the "Duke", the "Earl," and the "Count"?

10

Which virtuoso jazz drummer died in 1987?

11

In which country was Oscar Peterson born?

12

Which 1950s movie did wonders for the Newport Jazz Festival?

1

Which former jazz pianist became a classical conductor?

2

Who was best known as conductor of the Boston Pops Orchestra?

3

Who conducts the orchestra in the Disney movie *Fantasia*?

4

Which symphony orchestra did Eugene Ormandy conduct for 44 years?

5

Sir Georg Solti was principal conductor of which US orchestra?

6

Which conductor founded the London Philharmonic in 1932?

7

What nationality is the conductor Bernard Haitink?

8

Which legendary conductor was born in Salzburg in 1908?

9

Which great Italian conductor died in 1957 aged 89?

10

Which US musician was equally famous as conductor and composer?

11

For which famous conductor was the NBC Symphony Orchestra created?

12

Who became principal conductor of the Berlin Philharmonic in 2002?

1

Whose controversial 1980 release was called "Dirty Mind"?

2

Who had a hit with the theme song from the movie *Fame*?

3

What was the first-ever Western pop group to perform in China?

4

In which year did ABBA give their last public performance?

5

In which year was the MTV network launched?

6

In which 1987 movie is Dean Martin's "That's Amore" featured?

7

Who received an honorary knighthood for his charity work in 1986?

8

"Like A Virgin" was the unlikely named hit album for whom?

9

Who was Billy Joel singing about in "Uptown Girl"?

10

On which Bruce Springsteen album did "Atlantic City" feature?

11

What was Kylie Minogue's first hit single?

12

Which U2 album first made it to No 1 in the US?

1

In which country was Leonard Cohen born?

2

Which instrument did jazz musician John Coltrane play?

3

Who composed *The Love For Three Oranges*?

4

Who wrote the lyrics for the song "Hakuna Matata"?

5

What does the Japanese word *karaoke* mean?

6

Which 70s pop group regrouped for the 2007 Grammys?

7

Which movie introduced the song "White Christmas"?

8

Who wrote the song "Let's Do It, Let's Fall In Love"?

9

What was Johnny Mathis's 1976 Christmas offering?

10

Who did Reese Witherspoon play in the biopic *Walk the Line*?

11

Who died first, Gilbert or Sullivan?

12

Who were the song and dance duo of the stage show *Viva la Diva*?

1

Who composed the *Star Wars* theme?

2

Which musical instrument is featured in *The Third Man*?

3

In which movie is the song "Windmills of Your Mind"?

4

Whose music for *Atonement* won an Oscar in 2008?

5

Who composed the music for *Million Dollar Baby*?

6

Who sang the theme song from the Bond movie *License to Kill*?

7

What do the POWs whistle in *The Bridge Over the River Kwai*?

8

Whose music accompanied *The Sting*?

9

Who was the Oscar-winning composer for *Chariots of Fire*?

10

"I Need To Wake Up" was the wake-up call in which movie?

11

Who composed the music for *Gone With the Wind*?

12

Which composer do *Dr Zhivago* and *Lawrence of Arabia* share?

1

The opera *William Tell* was written by which composer?

2

Which famous European opera house was founded in 1778?

3

How many operas comprise Wagner's Ring cycle?

4

In the world of opera, what is a diva?

5

Who wrote the opera *The Tales of Hoffmann*?

6

What do the initials stand for in W S Gilbert?

7

How is the character Cio-Cio San better known?

8

Which Benjamin Britten opera is from a story by Herman Melville?

9

In the opera of the same name, what is Tosca's profession?

10

What is the text of an opera called?

11

Which great female opera singer was born in Sydney in 1926?

12

Which two Verdi operas are based on Shakespearean characters?

MUSIC
WHO COMPOSED THESE CLASSICS?

1

Peter and the Wolf

2

Carnival of the Animals

3

Young Person's Guide to the Orchestra

4

Arrival of the Queen of Sheba

5

Bolero

6

Appalachian Spring

7

Clair de Lune

8

Enigma Variations

9

The Stars and Stripes Forever

10

Academic Festival Overture

11

The Swan of Tuonela

12

On Hearing the First Cuckoo in Spring

1

Who shot to fame with their debut single "MmmmBop"?

2

Who wrote Sinéad O'Connor's 1990 hit "Nothing Compares 2 U"?

3

Who had the No 1 album hit "OK Computer" in 1997?

4

From which UK city did Noel and Liam Gallagher emerge?

5

Which duo had a smash hit in 1990 with "All My Love"?

6

Who sang "Black or White"?

7

Who appeared as JD in *Lock, Stock and Two Smoking Barrels*?

8

Which group embarked on a 30th anniversary tour in 1996?

9

"Love Is All Around" by Wet Wet Wet is in which 1994 movie?

10

Joe Cocker's "Delta Lady" is dedicated to which singer?

11

"Tuesday Night Music Club" was a 90s hit for whom?

12

What was the name of Annie Lennox's solo debut album?

1

Who composed the music for the ballet *Coppélia*?

2

Who is singer Nora Jones's famous father?

3

In the song, which river is "wider than a mile"?

4

Which hit for The Shadows is also a balsa raft?

5

What nationality was singer Jacques Brel?

6

Who is Elton John's long-time lyricist?

7

Larry Hagman is the son of which musical star?

8

What rap group recorded the hit album *Licensed to Kill*?

9

Who was the drummer in The Monkees?

10

In which movie did Elvis Presley play a boxer?

11

Which English classical violinist has a jazz combo?

12

Which country gave birth to Dame Kiri Te Kanawa?

1

Beethoven's fifth piano concerto is known as what?

2

Which 18th-century composer wrote more than 100 symphonies?

3

Who wrote "The Four Seasons"?

4

The "New World Symphony" is number what by Dvořák?

5

How many children did Johann Sebastian Bach have?

6

Which Rachmaninov piano concerto featured in *Brief Encounter*?

7

How many keys on a standard piano?

8

How many movements are there in Gustav Holst's "Planets Suite"?

9

How old was Mozart when he died?

10

Which Mahler symphony was used for the movie *Death in Venice*?

11

How many "Pomp and Circumstance" marches did Elgar compose?

12

What does Tchaikovsky's "1812 Overture" celebrate?

1

Who played Leather Tuscadero in *Happy Days*?

2

Who was the lead singer with Led Zeppelin?

3

Which former member of the Rolling Stones died in 1969?

4

In which movie did Elvis Presley make his screen debut?

5

Who recorded "Long Tall Sally" in 1956?

6

Which 1970s pop group had the name of a US bomber?

7

Whose debut solo album was titled "Faith"?

8

An assassination attempt was made on which singer's life in 1976?

9

Which group was Neil Young a member of before going solo?

10

Who wrote and sang the theme for the movie *Absolute Beginners*?

11

The BBC banned which 80s hit by Frankie Goes to Hollywood?

12

Which iconic rock festival took place in 1969?

1

Whose final concert tour lasted nearly three years?

2

In which city did Jim Morrison of The Doors die?

3

Where in New York was the original Cotton Club?

4

Who wrote the music for the movie *The Magnificent Seven*?

5

Who was Robert Goulet in the original production of *Camelot*?

6

What ageless song did Mildred and Patty Hill write in 1893?

7

Whose 2007 autobiography is titled *Unzipped*?

8

What musical instrument did comedian Jack Benny play?

9

Who was the vocalist in Genesis before Phil Collins?

10

Who was known as the "Clown Prince of Denmark"?

11

Who sang the theme from the Bond movie *From Russia with Love*?

12

How is French pianist Philippe Pages better known?

PEOPLE
ALL SORTS (1)

1

Which James wrote *Notes of a Native Son*?

2

Who said: "Genius is 99% perspiration and 1% inspiration"?

3

Ed McBain and Evan Hunter are pen names of which writer?

4

Which Russian dissident won the Nobel Peace Prize in 1975?

5

Which Irish playwright co-founded the London School of Economics?

6

Who was the fourth president?

7

What were the last names of Bonnie and Clyde?

8

Who was the love of William Randolph Hearst's life?

9

What nationality was St Thomas Aquinas?

10

Who was the first man to reach the South Pole?

11

Tony and Cherie Blair shared which profession?

12

What do the initials in E E Cummings stand for?

WHICH GEORGE?

1

Which George broke up with Andrew Ridgeley in 1986?

2

Which George wrote *St Joan*?

3

Which George was King of England in 1776?

4

Which George was a blind jazz pianist?

5

Which George wrote the Flashman novels?

6

Which George was a cigar-smoking comedian?

7

Which George lost the battle of the Little Bighorn?

8

Which George wrote the music while his brother wrote the words?

9

Which George was engaged to Linda Ronstadt?

10

Which George created a plan for Europe after World War II?

11

Which George directed the movie *Shane*?

12

Which George was a famous governor of Alabama?

1

Which movie couple married each other for a second time in 1975?

2

What was Romeo and Juliet's home town?

3

In which Scottish castle did Madonna and Guy Ritchie get married?

4

Which drama duo wrote *The Man Who Came to Dinner*?

5

Which royal couple celebrated their Golden Wedding in 1997?

6

Who lived longest, Stan Laurel or Oliver Hardy?

7

Who was the romantic inspiration for the Italian poet Dante?

8

Which Hollywood couple share the same birthday of September 25?

9

In which year did Sonny and Cher divorce?

10

Who was Joan Didion's co-writer husband who died in 2004?

11

What are the names of the Smothers Brothers?

12

Who married producer David Gest in 2002?

1

Who was the first man to fly solo across the Atlantic?

2

Who was the African American elected governor of a state?

3

Who was the first male to appear on the cover of *Playboy*?

4

Who was the first monarch to reside at Buckingham Palace?

5

Who was the first woman in space?

6

Who was the first prime minister of Israel?

7

Who was the first person to speak on the telephone?

8

Who was the first to open a five-and-dime store?

9

Who was the first person born in America to English parents?

10

Who was the first female speaker of the US House of Representatives?

11

Who was the first person to sail solo around the world?

12

Who was the first to swim the English Channel?

1

Who was the high-profile wife of Mikhail Gorbachev?

2

Who was America's first First Lady?

3

Which presidential wife dated Eric Clapton and Mick Jagger?

4

Which president's wife was named Bess?

5

Which presidential wife was an obsessive collector of shoes?

6

Which ex-wife of a president was sentenced to jail in 2003?

7

Which First Lady was a successful business entrepreneur?

8

Which wife of a president had a musical written about her?

9

Which president's wife was a real Dolley?

10

Which First Lady founded her own rehab center?

11

Which president's wife was executed with her husband in 1989?

12

Who became a UN delegate after she left the White House?

1

Which controversial comedian died of an overdose in 1966?

2

Who was John the Baptist's father?

3

Who has been called the father of the US air force?

4

Who wrote "The Battle Hymn of the Republic"?

5

What was Dwight D Eisenhower's original name?

6

Who pioneered frozen foods in the US?

7

Which English science-fiction writer was nicknamed "DNA"?

8

Who designed a push-up bra for Jane Russell?

9

Who was the US commander at the Battle of Cassino?

10

Which oil company was founded by John D Rockefeller?

11

Which reclusive American writer died in 2010?

12

Which French philosopher wrote: "I think therefore I am"?

PEOPLE
WHOSE LAST WORDS WERE THESE?

. . . .

1

"All my possessions for a moment of time."

. . . .

2

"I should never have switched from scotch to martinis."

. . . .

3

"Get my swan costume ready."

. . . .

4

"Rosebud."

. . . .

5

"God will pardon me, it is His trade."

. . . .

6

"Last words are for fools who haven't said enough."

. . . .

7

"I am still alive."

. . . .

8

"How were the receipts today at Madison Square Gardens?"

. . . .

9

"That was the best ice cream soda I ever tasted."

. . . .

10

"I shall hear in heaven."

. . . .

11

"That was a great game of golf, fellas."

. . . .

12

"The rest is silence."

. . . .

1

Who said: "England expects that every man will do his duty"?

2

Which US presidential candidate was a Vietnam war hero?

3

Which movie star was one of America's most decorated soldiers?

4

Which great orator and humanitarian began life as a slave?

5

In which country was American naval hero John Paul Jones born?

6

Which Apache hero's name means "One Who Yawns"?

7

Who was the founder of the nursing profession?

8

Marlon Brando portrayed which Mexican revolutionary hero on movie?

9

Which island won the George Cross for heroism in World War II?

10

Whose "midnight ride" in 1775 alerted the American rebels?

11

Which heroine of the civil rights movement died in 2005?

12

Who led the ill-fated expedition to the South Pole in 1911?

1

Which John always sang in black?

2

Which John assassinated Abraham Lincoln?

3

Which John's first major movie was *A Nightmare on Elm Street*?

4

Which John created Harry "Rabbit" Angstrom?

5

Which John was one of *The Dirty Dozen*?

6

Which John signed the Magna Carta?

7

Which John was a jazz saxophonist who died in 1967?

8

Which John is a classical guitarist?

9

Which John was a folk singer who died in a plane crash in 1997?

10

Which John won an Oscar for *Ryan's Daughter*?

11

Which John was a famous 20th-century UK economist?

12

Which John was "public enemy number one"?

PEOPLE
ALL SORTS (3)

1

Which famous English lovers poetically eloped in 1846?

2

What nationality was Winston Churchill's mother?

3

Which Russian czar murdered his own son?

4

What was Samuel Clemens' middle name?

5

Who is older, Mick Jagger or Paul McCartney?

6

Who was the first female US secretary of state?

7

Who was brother to the Brontë sisters?

8

Which princess rode for Britain in the Montreal Olympics?

9

A S Byatt is the sister of which other English novelist?

10

Who wrote: "To err is human, to forgive divine"?

11

Who directed the 1982 movie *Gandhi*?

12

The American classic *Tobacco Road* was written by whom?

120

PEOPLE
WHO DID THESE BECOME?

1

Joseph Ratzinger

2

William Jefferson Blythe

3

Nguyen Tat Thanh

4

Declan Patrick McManus

5

William Frederick Cody

6

Michael Shalhoub

7

Joseph Vissarionovich Djugashvili

8

Julia Elizabeth Wells

9

K'ung Fu-tzu

10

Martha Jane Cannary

11

William Perks

12

Margaret Hyra

1

Who killed Lee Harvey Oswald?

2

Which legendary bank robber did Lester M Gillis become?

3

Who was the "Oklahoma Bomber"?

4

Which New York serial killer became known as "Son of Sam"?

5

Who assassinated Martin Luther King?

6

What criminal career did the 18th-century Anne Bonny pursue?

7

How was Ilich Ramirez Sanchez better known?

8

For what crime was Al Capone convicted in 1931?

9

Who made London's Whitechapel his killing fields in the 1880s?

10

Whose escape from Devil's Island was a movie with Steve McQueen?

11

Which US serial killer gave himself an astrological nickname?

12

Who did John Hinckley Jr take a shot at in 1981?

1

What is the Queen of England's Scottish home?

2

What was Adolf Hitler's mountain retreat called?

3

Name the former Rockefeller family estate outside New York.

4

Which literary family lived at the rectory at Haworth?

5

Where is home to the French president?

6

Whose Mississippi home was called Rowan Oak?

7

Lawnfield in Mentor, Ohio was which president's home?

8

What is the country retreat of US presidents?

9

Which writer named his Hollywood home Ozcot?

10

La Casa Pacifica was whose "Western White House"?

11

Whose Caribbean home was called Goldeneye?

12

Who resides at No 11 Downing Street?

PEOPLE
ALL SORTS (4)

1

Whose real name was Claude William Dukenfield?

2

Which author and journalist became the man in the white suit?

3

Who was the first American World Chess Champion?

4

In which city was Raymond Chandler born?

5

Who compiled *The Devil's Dictionary*?

6

Who did starlet Valerie Solanis attempt to kill in 1968?

7

Who was Hubert Humphrey's running mate in the 1968 election?

8

What was Lenin's profession before becoming a revolutionary?

9

Tomáš Masaryk was the first president of which European country?

10

Which athlete's nickname was "Flo-Jo"?

11

Angelina Jolie's first child was adopted in which country?

12

In which country was composer Irving Berlin born?

PEOPLE
SHOWBIZ SIBLINGS: ADD THE SURNAME

1

Alec, Stephen, and William . . .

2

Ben and Casey . . .

3

Maxene, Patty, and Laverne . . .

4

Donnie & Mark . . .

5

Jake and Maggie . . .

6

Bruce, David, Keith, and Robert . . .

7

Eric and Julia . . .

8

James and John . . .

9

Alexis, David, Patricia, and Rosanna . . .

10

Joan and John . . .

11

Jane and Peter . . .

12

Andrew, Luke, and Owen . . .

125

PEOPLE
WHOSE NICKNAMES?

1
Papa

2
Bloody Mary

3
Louisville Lip

4
Chairman of the Board

5
The Ebony Express

6
Little Sparrow

7
Wizard of Menlo Park

8
Billy the Kid

9
The Divine Sarah

10
Bambi

11
The Italian Stallion

12
The Iron Butterfly

PEOPLE
WHAT A SCANDAL!

1

Which press tycoon and fraudster mysteriously died at sea in 1991?

2

Who blew the whistle on Monica Lewinsky and Bill Clinton?

3

Which sporting star fathered a child in a closet?

4

Which Hollywood star was jailed in 1948 on a drugs' charge?

5

Which TV evangelist's fling with a call girl took him off air?

6

Which super model earned 200 hours community service in 2008?

7

Who ended Gary Hart's presidential hopes in 1987?

8

Which movie star's daughter killed gangster Johnny Stompanato?

9

What undesirable hit list did Burt Reynolds get on to in 2009?

10

Who was the American TV lifestyle guru sent to jail in 2004?

11

Who was the woman in the 1921 Fatty Arbuckle affair?

12

What was author Jeffrey Archer imprisoned for in 2001?

PEOPLE
ALL SORTS (5)

1

What were the names of the flying Wright Brothers?

2

In which year did Britain's Queen Mother reach her century?

3

Who is the patron saint of lost causes?

4

Which actor died during the filming of *Gladiator* in 1999?

5

Whose 1950s novel *The Naked Lunch* was initially banned in the US?

6

What do the initials stand for in E B White?

7

Which role did Phil Collins play on stage in *Oliver*?

8

Who was on the cover of the first issue of *Playboy* magazine?

9

Which great Austrian composer taught both Mozart and Beethoven?

10

Who was elected president of Poland in 1990?

11

In which movie did Daniel Radcliffe make his screen debut?

12

Which president was a former director of the CIA?

128 PEOPLE
WHO SAID THESE?

1

"They misunderestimated me."

2

"Anyone who says he can see through a woman is missing a lot."

3

"Don't count the days, make the days count."

4

"I'm a Ford, not a Lincoln."

5

"Nothing happened in the sixties except that we all dressed up."

6

"Money is better than poverty, if only for financial reasons."

7

"Politics is too serious a matter to be left to the politicians."

8

"When the President does it, that means that it's not illegal."

9

"I have never delivered a firebrand speech."

10

"A wide screen just makes a bad movie twice as bad."

11

"Power is the ultimate aphrodisiac."

12

"As God once said, and I think rightly . . . "

PEOPLE
WHICH HENRY?

1

Which Henry has a river named after him?

2

Which Henry shared the Nobel Peace Prize in 1973?

3

Which Henry was the victor at Agincourt in 1415?

4

Which Henry composed the Pink Panther theme?

5

Which Henry is associated with Big Sur, California?

6

Which Henry directed the classic war movie *Twelve O'clock High*?

7

Which Henry was called "The Great Pacificator"?

8

Which Henry wrote *The Turn of the Screw*?

9

Which Henry became US ambassador to the UN in 1953?

10

Which Henry practiced household management in the woods?

11

Which Henry wrote a nine-volume history of the United States?

12

Which Henry was given Hampton Court Palace as a gift?

1

In Greek mythology, who was enchanted with his own reflection?

2

Which god drove the chariot of the sun across the sky?

3

How many tasks did Hercules have to perform?

4

Who stole fire from Mount Olympus to give to mankind?

5

Which Greek god was known as the "Earthshaker"?

6

Who was the Norse god of thunder?

7

What was the prize in the Judgement of Paris?

8

Who took 20 years to return home from the Trojan War?

9

Who ferried the souls of the dead across the River Styx?

10

Which Egyptian goddess had the head of a cat?

11

Who had the golden touch?

12

Which Greek deity equated with the Roman god Mercury?

1

Whose soul goes marching on?

2

Who was the first man to reach the top of Mount Everest?

3

On whose novel was the movie *Master and Commander* based?

4

Who was the governor of Louisiana assassinated in 1935?

5

Which author won the Nobel Prize in Literature in 1938?

6

Kim Basinger's daughter shares the name of which country?

7

Who was the founder of the Boy Scout movement?

8

Which of the play-writing Shaffer twins wrote *Sleuth*?

9

Who became Germany's first woman chancellor in 2005?

10

What is Rupert Murdoch's first name?

11

Who is Tara Newley's famous mother?

12

Who proposed as her epitaph: "Excuse my dust"?

SCIENCE & NATURE
RANDOM SAMPLE (1)

1

To what family do cabbages and cauliflowers belong?

2

What is a beaver's home called?

3

The kiwi uses which sense to hunt for food?

4

What is the medical term for drilling a hole in the skull?

5

Becquerels are a unit of what?

6

Which salad item is *nasturtium officinale*?

7

The word vaccination comes from the Latin name for which animal?

8

What blocks the sun's ultra-violet rays?

9

What animal did the Russians send into space in 1957?

10

What is endocrinology?

11

Mulefoot and Red Wattle are breeds of what animal?

12

Which bird can swim but can't fly?

1

From which plant does belladonna come?

2

What does the herb borage taste like?

3

What is the world's hardest and heaviest wood?

4

What species of tree is the "General Sherman"?

5

What part of a plant produces pollen?

6

How many petals on a wild orchid?

7

What plants have neither flowers nor roots?

8

Californian, Yellow Horned, and Opium are types of what?

9

What is the largest seed in the plant kingdom?

10

What plant devours insects?

11

What fungus is used in the production of alcohol?

12

Where do peanut pods ripen?

1

Which garden insect belongs to the locust family?

2

What is the horn of a rhinoceros made from?

3

Where does a "demersal" creature live?

4

Which bear is bigger—brown, grizzly or polar?

5

What kind of feet do palmipeds have?

6

Which animal can be Red, Arctic, Bat-eared, and Fennec?

7

What is a badger's home called?

8

Which Australian animal's name means "no drink"?

9

Which is the only bird that can fly backward?

10

The mule is a cross between what?

11

What are arachnids?

12

A glow-worm is not a worm—what is it?

SCIENCE & NATURE
IDENTIFY THE MISSING COLLECTIVE NAMES

1

A pod of . . .

2

A knot of . . .

3

A farrow of . . .

4

A chatter of . . .

5

An ambush of . . .

6

A tower of . . .

7

A plague of . . .

8

A smack of . . .

9

A clowder of . . .

10

A bouquet of. . .

11

A crash of. . .

12

A tittering of . . .

136

. . . .

1

What is the longest bone in the body?

. . . .

2

Where is the thyroid gland?

. . . .

3

How many chambers does the heart have?

. . . .

4

Where in the body is the labyrinth?

. . . .

5

What are inflamed if you suffer from nephritis?

. . . .

6

How many chromosomes are there in the human body?

. . . .

7

What does REM stand for?

. . . .

8

Who has more ribs, a man or a woman?

. . . .

9

Which hemisphere of the brain controls the left half of the body?

. . . .

10

What is the largest organ in the body?

. . . .

11

What is another name for cartilage?

. . . .

12

Which gland produces insulin?

. . . .

SCIENCE & NATURE
RANDOM SAMPLE (2)

1

Who discovered carbon dioxide in 1754?

2

Which nocturnal bird has a distinctive three-syllable call?

3

What do silkworms feed on?

4

Who was the last man on the moon?

5

What is the world's smallest bird?

6

Acid turns litmus paper which color?

7

What is carrageen also known as?

8

What was built to test the "Big Bang" theory?

9

What species of mammal is a lemming?

10

Solid carbon dioxide is known by what name?

11

Bronze is a combination of which two metals?

12

The call of which bird resembles human laughter?

1

What does a pluviometer measure?

2

What is the highest cloud formation?

3

What number on the Beaufort Scale denotes a gale?

4

What are the Sirocco and Mistral?

5

What do isobars measure?

6

What is an area of high atmospheric pressure called?

7

The Mercalli Scale is used for measuring what?

8

What was successfully launched on April 1 1960?

9

What was the name of the 2005 hurricane that hit New Orleans?

10

Most tornadoes in the Northern Hemisphere spin which way?

11

What is humidity?

12

What is the irregular Pacific Ocean current that affects weather?

1

What family of plant is bamboo?

2

Where were satsumas first cultivated?

3

What moss is found in peat bogs?

4

The pohutukawa tree is native to which country?

5

Which part of a flower protects its bud?

6

Polenta flour came originally from the seed of which tree?

7

What was the kiwi fruit originally called?

8

How is the Lent Lily better known?

9

What is a puffball?

10

What part of the oak tree is used for tanning leather?

11

What part of a plant catches pollen?

12

On which continent will you find the monkey bread tree?

1

Where is a rattlesnake's rattle located?

2

What is a baby whale called?

3

Which insect performs the Waggle Dance?

4

What species of animal is a porcupine?

5

Which island did the dodo originally inhabit?

6

What is the covering of a deer's antler called?

7

How many arms does a starfish have?

8

What animal is a *Canus lupus*?

9

Which animal was domesticated first, the dog or the cat?

10

What is another name for the wapiti?

11

Which animal's droppings are called spraint?

12

Which water creature shares its name with a Florida river?

1

What is a baby alligator called?

2

What does a BCG vaccination protect you against?

3

Cinnamon and Silver Fox are breeds of which animal?

4

What are Saturn's rings made of?

5

Rickets is caused by a deficiency of which vitamin?

6

What did Wilhelm Röntgen invent?

7

What is the layman's term for nitrous oxide?

8

Heavy water is used in the development of what?

9

In computer terminology, what does HTML stand for?

10

How many pounds are there in 10 kilograms?

11

What is a butterfly pupa called?

12

Which element has the atomic number "1"?

1

What is the world's fastest mammal?

2

What is the world's largest bird of prey?

3

Which dinosaur had the longest tail?

4

What is the world's largest mammal?

5

Which elephant has the biggest ears, African or Indian?

6

Which insect has the shortest life?

7

What is the largest tree fruit in the world?

8

What is the world's slowest mammal?

9

What is the longest snake in the world?

10

What is the world's largest lizard?

11

Which insect is the longest in the world?

12

What is the world's fastest creature?

1

Who is known as "The Father of Medicine"?

2

Where is the occipital bone located in the human body?

3

Which disease affects the salivary glands?

4

What is the varicella zoster virus more commonly called?

5

What drug is used to treat malaria?

6

Who carried out the first heart transplant in 1967?

7

In which year was the first test-tube baby delivered?

8

What is Computerised Axial Tomography?

9

What are you having if you suffer a myocardial infarction?

10

What is gypsum also known as?

11

What is an Ishihara Test used for?

12

Which plant produces the heart stimulant digitalis?

1

Name the space telescope launched in 1990.

2

Which is the largest planet in the solar system?

3

What is a supernova?

4

Would a lake on Mars be freezing or boiling?

5

Which comet was highly visible from Earth in 1997?

6

What does the "Bishop's Ring" encircle?

7

Which galaxy is nearest to our own?

8

What is the most abundant element in the universe?

9

How long does it take for sunlight to reach Earth?

10

What planet is often referred to as the Morning Star?

11

Where would you find the "Marsh of Sleep"?

12

What is the Latin name for the Northern Lights?

SCIENCE & NATURE
RANDOM SAMPLE (4)

1

What gives plants their green color?

2

Hydrophobia is another name for what?

3

How does a digitigrade animal walk?

4

What is a Speckled Racer?

5

What are Tussock, Burnet, and Goat species of?

6

What is 0° Fahrenheit in centigrade?

7

Which gas forms nearly 80% of the earth's atmosphere?

8

Silicon Valley is adjacent to which city?

9

What does FM stand for in radio?

10

Who became known as "Father of the Atom Bomb"?

11

Scurvy is caused by a deficiency of which vitamin?

12

What was the name of the first cloned sheep?

1

Where is the smallest muscle located?

2

What is the larynx?

3

Which part of the eye contains no blood vessels?

4

What is the average number of hairs on the head?

5

What are the soft spots called on a newborn baby's skull?

6

What is the epidermis?

7

What part of the tongue tastes sweet things?

8

What are the three kinds of teeth (excluding false!)?

9

What is a *latissimus dorsi*?

10

Tinnitus affects which of the senses?

11

What do you actually aggravate when you hit your "funny bone"?

12

What is the hardest material in the human body?

1

Which husband and wife won the Nobel Prize for Physics in 1903?

2

Who defined the law of universal gravitation?

3

Who discovered oxygen in 1774?

4

What did Alexander Fleming discover in 1928?

5

Who wrote *The Interpretation of Dreams*?

6

Who created the first smallpox vaccine?

7

Which great scientist and philosopher was born in Pisa in 1564?

8

Who was the first man to split the atom?

9

Who in 1628 plotted the circulation of blood in the body?

10

Who pioneered the use of antiseptics?

11

What is Albert Einstein best known for?

12

What nationality was the astronomer Nicolaus Copernicus?

SCIENCE & NATURE
PHOBIAS: WHAT ARE YOU AFRAID OF?

1

Ailurophobia

2

Xenophobia

3

Tachophobia

4

Arachnophobia

5

Cyberphobia

6

Gamophobia

7

Apiphobia

8

Hippophobia

9

Hydrophobia

10

Photophobia

11

Ophthalmophobia

12

Phobophobia

1

What is a squirrel's nest called?

2

Which planet's orbit is closest to the sun?

3

What does DVD stand for?

4

The Cephalic Index relates to measuring what part of the body?

5

Where is the home of the Prime Meridian?

6

What is a river otter's nest called?

7

Which element has the highest melting point?

8

Ursine describes which type of animal?

9

Who invented the telegraph code?

10

What is the world's largest fish?

11

In which country was barley first grown?

12

What is ornithology the study of?

SCIENCE & NATURE
STRANGE BUT TRUE

1

What is the male honeybee's only role in life?

2

Which insect can jump 130 times its own height?

3

Which sea creature spends its life standing on its head?

4

From what part of Canada do Labrador dogs come?

5

Which fish spends much of its time out of water?

6

What creature has no brain or heart and consists mainly of water?

7

Which birds never need to drink fresh water?

8

How many eyes do most species of spiders have?

9

Which is the only male creature to give birth?

10

Which common insect has taste buds on its feet?

11

Which sea creature has enough power to illuminate a house?

12

What do queen ants lose after mating?

151

SCIENCE & NATURE
GREAT INVENTORS

1

Whose vision created television?

2

What did Tim Berners-Lee invent in 1989?

3

Who built the first successful steam locomotive?

4

What did Sir Frank Whittle invent in 1928?

5

Who in 1835 came up with the revolver?

6

What did Sir Christopher Cockerell launch in 1956?

7

Who pioneered wireless telegraphy?

8

What did Nicolas-Jacques Conté invent in 1795?

9

Whose 15th-century invention made this book possible?

10

Who invented the safety razor?

11

Whose brainchild was the mercury thermometer?

12

What revolutionary camera did Edwin Land invent?

152

SCIENCE & NATURE

WHAT WOULD YOU BE STUDYING?

1
Vulcanology

2
Entomology

3
Podology

4
Seismology

5
Conchology

6
Cetology

7
Otology

8
Palaeoanthropology

9
Nephology

10
Metrology

11
Heliology

12
Ombrology

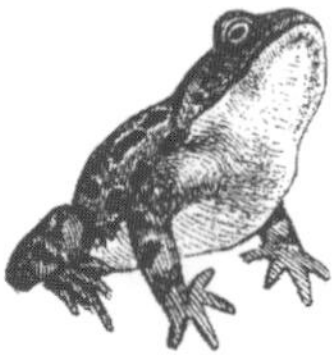

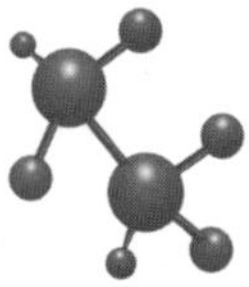

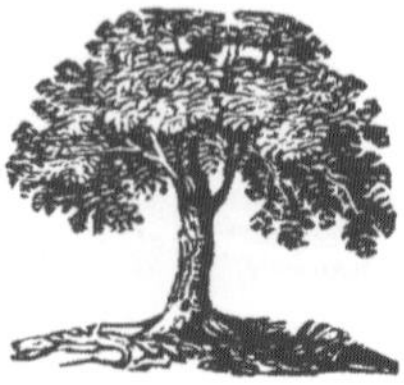

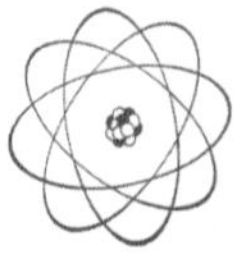

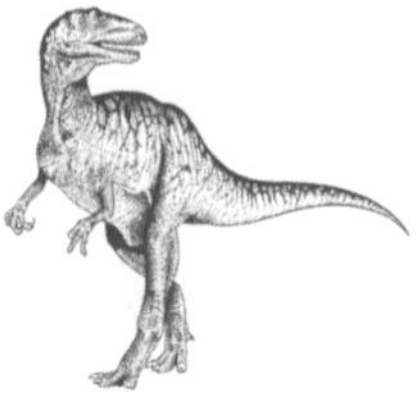

1

What kind of animal is an opossum?

2

The ohm is a measurement of what?

3

What did Francis Crick and James Watson unravel?

4

Mexican Spotted, Lesser Sooty, and Burrowing are types of what?

5

Which is the brightest star in the night sky?

6

What does an arboretum consist of?

7

What is a baby hare called?

8

What is the symbol for tin in the periodic table?

9

What medical instrument did Théophile-Hyacinthe Laënnec invent?

10

Which flower's name comes from the French for "lion's tooth"?

11

What vegetable is a *Solanum tuberosum*?

12

What is a "growler"?

SPORTS & GAMES
SPORTING CHANCE (1)

1

In 1845 Alexander Cartwright wrote the rules for which game?

2

Who said: "The bigger they come, the harder they fall"?

3

How many red cards are there in a standard pack?

4

The FIDE is the governing body of which board game?

5

Who was the first man to hit a golf ball on the moon?

6

Which father and son were Formula One world champions?

7

Who was the first woman to run a mile in under five minutes?

8

Philippa Roberts was a world champion in which sport?

9

What sporting weapon fires a quarrel?

10

In which year did Cassius Clay become Muhammad Ali?

11

How old was Michael Phelps when he competed in his first Olympics?

12

In which city were the 1920 Olympic Games held?

1

Who wrote the first published rules on baseball?

2

What was "Babe" Ruth's full name?

3

In which year was the modern World Series established?

4

Who was known as "Knucksie"?

5

Which New York Yankee had a cartoon character named after him?

6

In baseball jargon, what is a "yakker"?

7

Name the first African-American officially to play major league.

8

For which major-league side did Carl Yastrzemski play?

9

In which year was the Baseball Hall of Fame inaugurated?

10

Who was the first to win the World Series in the new millennium?

11

In which year did baseball become an official Olympic sport?

12

Who was the first major-league player in the 4000 hits club?

1

In which year was the first Super Bowl?

2

Who said: "Winning isn't everything, it's the only thing"?

3

In which two events did Jim Thorpe win Olympic golds in 1912?

4

Which "Bus" came to a stop in 2006?

5

After which player was the Green Bay Packers' stadium named?

6

What in football is known as a "bomb"?

7

In which country was Knute Rockne born?

8

At which university did Jim Brown make his name?

9

Which was the first NFL game to go into sudden death overtime?

10

Which former football star played a former basketball star on TV?

11

Who was the first "Super Bowl Most Valuable Player"?

12

In a football game, who are the "zebras"?

1

What are the three main types of golf clubs?

2

What is an "eagle"?

3

British and US women golfers compete for which trophy?

4

In which "Open" does the victor win his weight in cheese?

5

Who was the first left-hander to win a major championship?

6

Which golfer was nicknamed "The Great White Shark"?

7

Who won the 2008 US Masters?

8

In which year did the Ryder Cup begin?

9

Who won her first Women's British Open in 1995?

10

What in golfing parlance is an "ace"?

11

Where is the oldest public golf course in the US?

12

Which great US golfer died in September 2006?

SPORTS & GAMES
BASKETBALL

1

What did the Savoy Big Five become?

2

In which country was Nathan Jawai born?

3

At which Olympics did Michael Jordan win his first gold medal?

4

In which year was the first women's world championship?

5

In basketball slang, what is a "T"?

6

Which team won the first NBA championship in 1947?

7

What were basketball inventor James Naismith's first baskets?

8

Who was the "Houdini of the Hardwood"?

9

How tall was the former Romanian player Gheorghe Mureşan?

10

What was the first country after the US to win the Olympics?

11

Who appeared bedridden in *Curb Your Enthusiasm*?

12

Who in 1960 became basketball's first World Champions?

SPORTS & GAMES
SPORTING CHANCE (2)

1

What surface is curling played on?

2

Who was "Pistol Pete"?

3

Who captained the US Ryder Cup team in 2006?

4

Who was the first World Chess Champion?

5

When a judo referee says *hajime* what does it mean?

6

Complete this football team's name: Minnesota . . .

7

Which US weightlifter set 16 world records in his career?

8

Jansher and Jahangir Khan are famous in which sport?

9

Who is the movie *Somebody Up There Likes Me* about?

10

Which team won the America's Cup for the second time in 2000?

11

What sport takes place in a velodrome?

12

Where did Woody Hayes become a legendary coach?

1

In which year did Jenson Button win his first Grand Prix?

2

Where was Ayrton Senna killed in 1994?

3

Who was the first Formula One world champion?

4

During a race, what does a blue flag indicate to a driver?

5

What nationality was racing driver Emerson Fittipaldi?

6

"Brain fade" is motor-racing slang for what?

7

Which French motor race lasts for 24 hours?

8

What is the Italian Grand Prix circuit?

9

Who posthumously won the F1 World Championship in 1970?

10

Which French driver had a career total of 51 Grand Prix wins?

11

In which year was the Indianapolis 500 first staged?

12

Who was the first US driver to win the F1 World Championship?

SPORTS & GAMES
TENNIS: 1ST SET

1

What is Andy Murray's tennis-playing brother's name?

2

What is the regulation height of a tennis net at the center?

3

How many singles titles did Martina Navratilova win?

4

Which tennis star was stabbed on court in 1993?

5

Complete the duo—Newcombe and . . .

6

What is the second Grand Slam event of the year?

7

What nationality is Justine Henin?

8

Who was unseeded when he won his first Wimbledon singles title?

9

Which tennis player did Chris Evert marry in 1979?

10

Which country won the Davis Cup in 2008?

11

Under which name did Billie Jean King first play?

12

How many times did John McEnroe win the US Open singles title?

SPORTS & GAMES
THE OLYMPICS

1

What do the five Olympic rings represent?

2

Where and in what year were the first Olympic Games in the US?

3

Who was stripped of his gold medal at the Seoul Olympics?

4

How long is an Olympic marathon (to the nearest mile/kilometre)?

5

How many Olympic gold medals did Tarzan win?

6

Why did several countries boycott the 1956 Olympics?

7

Where and in what year were the first-ever winter Olympics?

8

Jesse Owens won gold medals in which four events?

9

Which gymnast uniquely achieved a perfect score twice in 1976?

10

In which year did Cassius Clay win an Olympic gold?

11

Who was known as "The Flying Housewife"?

12

What does an Olympic gold medal mainly consist of?

SPORTS & GAMES
SPORTING CHANCE (3)

1

Whose nickname was "The Big Easy"?

2

What nationality was tennis star Maria Bueno?

3

Who gets to lift the Vince Lombardi Trophy?

4

What sport did Dr James Naismith found in 1891?

5

How many oars are used in sculling?

6

What is the inside diameter of a basketball hoop?

7

How long did the 1981 US baseball strike last?

8

What material is used to make a sumo wrestling ring?

9

In which Asian country is the Blue Canyon golf course?

10

What is the alternative name for a castle in chess?

11

When was Lance Armstrong's first win in the Tour de France?

12

Whose ear did Mike Tyson notoriously bite?

164

SPORTS & GAMES
WHICH SPORTS FEATURED IN THESE MOVIES?

1

The Natural

2

The Pride of the Yankees

3

International Velvet

4

Slap Shot

5

The Longest Yard

6

Breaking Away

7

The Set-Up

8

Hoosiers

9

Big Wednesday

10

Seabiscuit

11

White Men Can't Jump

12

Chariots of Fire

1

Who was known as "The Big Train"?

2

In which year was the Black Sox scandal?

3

Which team won the 1938 baseball World Series?

4

What put Eddie Gaedel into the record books?

5

Which Hollywood star bought the Los Angeles Angels in 1961?

6

Who broke Lou Gehrig's consecutive game record in 1995?

7

What will earn you a "golden sombrero"?

8

What innovatory baseball league was launched in 1943?

9

Who had a grand total of 755 home runs in his career?

10

How many Cy Young awards did Roger Clemens win?

11

What handicap did major-league pitcher Jim Abbott overcome?

12

Who played Babe Ruth in the movie *The Babe*?

1

In football, which animals come from Detroit?

2

Name the first running back to gain over 2,000 yards in a season.

3

Who was first president of the American Professional FA?

4

Whose nickname was "Night Train"?

5

Football wise, Gerald Ford and Jack Kerouac have what in common?

6

Name the first winners of the Super Bowl.

7

Who were the first winners of the World Bowl?

8

Who holds the record for playing the most seasons in the NFL?

9

In which year did the AFL and NFL merge?

10

In which country was placekicker Gary Anderson born?

11

How did Knute Rockne die?

12

Whose 1993 NFL comeback against Houston was the biggest ever?

1

In which sport would you perform a salchow?

2

What is the start of a hockey match called?

3

Which jockey was called "The Kentucky Kid"?

4

What do the players strike in badminton?

5

Complete this US baseball team's name: Minnesota . . .

6

How many times did Sonny Liston fight Floyd Patterson?

7

Who did the US beat in their first-ever rugby World Cup victory?

8

Who won more tennis Grand Slam titles, Boris Becker or John McEnroe?

9

In archery, what are fletchings?

10

In which sport would you need a foil or an épée?

11

In which year were the Olympics held in Mexico?

12

In what sport at the 1912 Olympics did a match last 11h 40min?

SPORT & GAMES
GOLF: 2ND ROUND

1

Where is the home of the Royal and Ancient Golf Club?

2

Where was the first US Open staged in 1895?

3

What is the maximum number of clubs allowed in a bag?

4

Who was the first non-American to win the US Masters?

5

In which year did Team Europe first contest the Ryder Cup?

6

What is the term for going three under par on a hole?

7

Who was the first golfer to win $1m in prize money?

8

Which American cricket club has been the venue for the US Open?

9

Which golfer made plus fours the on-course fashion?

10

In which year did Bobby Jones win the first-ever Grand Slam?

11

Who became the first Irishman to win The Open for 60 years?

12

In which country is the World Ice Golf Championship held?

SPORTS & GAMES
HOCKEY

1

How many players are there in an hockey team?

2

What is a "blueliner"?

3

Which country in 1936 interrupted Canada's run of Olympic titles?

4

What was the World Cup of Hockey previously known as?

5

Who is annually awarded the Hart Memorial Trophy?

6

Who bought the Pittsburgh Penguins in 1999?

7

In which city was the first organized game of hockey played?

8

Who was the first European to win the Art Ross Trophy?

9

What did Canada's governor general give the sport in 1892?

10

Against whom did Sidney Crosby score his first NHL hat trick?

11

Who was dubbed "Mr Hockey"?

12

Which men's team won gold at the 2006 Winter Olympics?

1

Moving clockwise on a dartboard, what number is next to 1?

2

In the world of pool, who is the "Duchess of Doom"?

3

Name the odd one out: king, queen, bishop, cardinal?

4

In which country did the card game Canasta originate?

5

How many squares on a standard checkers board?

6

In which card game does Omar Sharif excel?

7

Which game takes its name from the Chinese for "sparrow"?

8

In poker, what hand beats a straight flush?

9

Who became the undisputed world chess champion in 2006?

10

What is a grand slam in bridge?

11

How many object balls are there in eight-ball pool?

12

In which game is there a "Doubling Cube"?

1

Over what distance is the Kentucky Derby run?

2

In which sport would you see a Fosbury Flop?

3

How many times did Jackie Stewart win the F1 World Championship?

4

In what year was the first Tour de France cycle race?

5

In swimming, what is the trudgen?

6

In which year did the US host soccer's FIFA World Cup?

7

Who were the two athletic heroes of *Chariots of Fire*?

8

What is rolled in the Canadian sport of birling?

9

What is a Boston crab?

10

What annual rowing event first took place in 1829?

11

Who won seven gold medals at the 1972 Olympics?

12

Whose first win in a golf major was the 2005 US Open?

SPORTS & GAMES
NAME THE SPORT ASSOCIATED WITH THESE VENUES

1

The Palestra

2

Fenway Park

3

Los Angeles Memorial Coliseum

4

Caesars Palace

5

Pebble Beach

6

Maple Leaf Gardens

7

Talladega

8

Valderrama

9

Rucker Park

10

Bethpage Black

11

Wrigley Field

12

Melbourne Park

1

Who uniquely won world championships on both two and four wheels?

2

What nationality was racing driver Jody Scheckter?

3

Which Formula One team had the name of a sacred flower?

4

Which US Formula One world champion was born in Italy?

5

What did the Formula One team Elf-Tyrrell introduce in 1976?

6

Where did the first F1 American Grand Prix take place?

7

Who became the first driver to win six times in a row at Le Mans?

8

By how much did Al Unser beat Scott Goodyear in the 1992 Indy 500?

9

Which US race takes place annually over Memorial Day weekend?

10

Where in China was the first Grand Prix staged in 2004?

11

Which was Michael Schumacher's first Formula One winning team?

12

Who was the first woman to compete in the Indianapolis 500?

1

Which women's tennis player won double gold at the 1924 Olympics?

2

What was Althea Gibson's first record-breaking Grand Slam title?

3

How long between Jimmy Connors' two Wimbledon singles titles?

4

Who was nicknamed "The Terminator"?

5

Which future English monarch played at Wimbledon in 1926?

6

Who is the only player to have achieved two calendar Grand Slams?

7

Who was the first player to serve over 1000 aces in a season?

8

Which Australian tennis star became Mrs Roger Cawley?

9

Who did Roger Federer beat in his first Wimbledon final?

10

Who became the youngest-ever US Open champion in 1979?

11

Which US tennis star of the 1920s died in poverty in 1953?

12

What nationality is Marcos Baghdatis?

1

Which heavyweight was known as "The Ambling Alp"?

2

What age was Archie Moore when he fought Cassius Clay in 1962?

3

Which world champion retired undefeated in February 2009?

4

How many times did Sugar Ray Robinson beat Jake LaMotta?

5

Who defeated Joe Louis in his comeback fight in 1950?

6

What is the lightest weight category in professional boxing?

7

Which British champion did Mike Tyson beat in 1989?

8

Which world champion heavyweight's real name was Arnold Cream?

9

What does a boxer have to achieve to be a Triple Champion?

10

How did Rocky Marciano die?

11

For which country did Lennox Lewis win gold in the 1988 Olympics?

12

Which British boxer dubbed himself "Prince"?

1

What is the longest-running trophy in international sport?

2

What do baseball players call a "dinger"?

3

Which female athlete was famous for running barefoot?

4

Which 1950s Czech tennis champion represented Egypt?

5

What is an oxer?

6

In which year did Tiger Woods win his first major?

7

Where did the game pelota originate?

8

What was swimmer Enrico Tiraboschi the first to do in 1923?

9

Whose 19th-century rules for boxing are still in use today?

10

What sport is divided into chukkas?

11

What in hockey is the "cage"?

12

Which women's tennis star retired for a second time in 2007?

1

What does ECG stand for?

2

When was the Frisbee invented?

3

Which nation first gave women the right to vote?

4

What is the next prime number after 71?

5

Complete this football team's name: Arizona . . .

6

Where were the Bee Gees born?

7

Which household item is made from naphthalene?

8

What is the most common non-contagious disease?

9

Which liqueur is used in a Sidecar cocktail?

10

Which instrument did Lionel Hampton play?

11

Who led a slave revolt in Virginia in 1831?

12

What is the first name of the French artist Cézanne?

1

What was once called brimstone?

2

How many sides are there in a pair of nonagons?

3

Who was Peeping Tom peeping at?

4

What color is carmine?

5

What is the art of shaping hedges called?

6

Love Apple is an old-fashioned name for what?

7

What does *Götterdämmerung* mean?

8

Who wrote the 1970s novel *Fear of Flying*?

9

On which geological fault line is San Francisco?

10

What are Moss, Garter, and Cable types of?

11

Which famous cat was created by Otto Messmer?

12

What did Jerry's Guide to the World Wide Web become?

1

To which flower family does garlic belong?

2

Who in 1991 became France's first woman prime minister?

3

What relation is Liza Minnelli to Lorna Luft?

4

How did soul singer Sam Cooke die?

5

What trees can grow above the tree line?

6

Who designed a seaplane called "The Spruce Goose"?

7

What is the alcoholic ingredient in a Snowball cocktail?

8

What was the name of Gene Autry's horse?

9

What does MCC add up to in roman numerals?

10

Which playwright became his country's president in 1989?

11

Name the winged horse in Greek mythology.

12

Which ex-wife of a president was sentenced to jail in 2003?

GENERAL KNOWLEDGE
NUMBER 4

1

Which butterfly has the same name as a punctuation mark?

2

What is the capital of Uzbekistan?

3

For how many years was Robinson Crusoe marooned?

4

Which Netherlands city is famous for its porcelain?

5

Name the three wise men of the Nativity story.

6

What is Miss Piggy's last name?

7

Which First Lady founded her own rehab centre?

8

Who did Nicolas Sarkozy succeed as French president?

9

What is the provincial capital of Alberta in Canada?

10

What is campanology?

11

What is the calendar used by most Western nations?

12

What does the Japanese word *kamikaze* mean?

GENERAL KNOWLEDGE
NUMBER 5

1

Who was New Zealand's first woman prime minister?

2

What is the chemical symbol for potassium?

3

Which girl's name means "my father rejoices"?

4

What is dactylology?

5

Who was Robin Hood's arch enemy?

6

Which language has the most native speakers?

7

Where is known as "The Great White Way"?

8

Which breed of dog was Winston Churchill likened to?

9

Who played the butler in the TV series *Hart to Hart*?

10

On which river does Rome stand?

11

What does Volkswagen mean?

12

What do the Four Horsemen of the Apocalypse represent?

1

How many books are there in the New Testament?

2

Which grow upwards, stalactites or stalagmites?

3

In which ocean is the Gulf Stream?

4

Who was the manager of the Sex Pistols?

5

Which famous riding school is in Vienna?

6

What did the pope become in 1870?

7

A Turk's Head is a type of what?

8

How was Julius Garfinkle better known?

9

Who wrote the original Bambi book?

10

What is a gallivat?

11

To which actress was David Frost engaged in the 1970s?

12

What Italian city is home to the Fiat car?

1

What does VSOP stand for on a bottle of brandy?

2

On whose Berlin stories was the musical *Cabaret* based?

3

How is Lesley Hornby better known?

4

In heraldry, what color is sable?

5

What is the collective noun for kangaroos?

6

Who invented the lightning conductor?

7

In which Indian city is the Sikh religion's Golden Temple?

8

Who composed the *March Slav*?

9

Which German spa gave its name to an item of men's headwear?

10

Which 60s pop duo changed their name from Tom and Jerry?

11

In Morse code, what letter is represented by four dots?

12

How many biblical plagues of Egypt were there?

1

Name the six annual Nobel Prize categories.

2

What do "almost" and "biopsy" have in common?

3

Who did Dick Van Dyke play in *The Dick Van Dyke Show*?

4

Which of the Seven Wonders of the World was at Olympia?

5

Which artist painted his *Bedroom in Arles*?

6

Who was the South African prime minister assassinated in 1966?

7

What is the symbol of the World Wildlife Fund?

8

Which Russian novelist wrote *The Government Inspector*?

9

What do the initials FLAG stand for?

10

What is the knife carried by Gurkha soldiers called?

11

Who had a 1950s hit with "Dream Lover"?

12

Who is the patron saint of taxi drivers?

GENERAL KNOWLEDGE
NUMBER 9

1

What was Dr Josef Mengele called?

2

What is the name of David and Victoria Beckham's third son?

3

The island of Zanzibar is part of which country?

4

What does a notaphile collect?

5

Which English explorer was killed in Hawaii in 1779?

6

Who directed the film *Halloween*?

7

What is usually kept in a bandbox?

8

Which military force protects the Vatican and the Pope?

9

Who had a 1980s hit with "Stand And Deliver"?

10

Who are Huey, Dewey, and Louie?

11

On which day of the week did Solomon Grundy marry?

12

In Hawaiian, does *aloha* mean hello or goodbye?

1

What is the larger bottle, a methuselah or a nebuchadnezzar?

2

How many times were Torvill and Dean World Ice Dance Champions?

3

Who was India's first prime minister?

4

Who won the 2006 Masters golf championship?

5

In which country were Venetian blinds invented?

6

The mythological centaur is part man and part what?

7

What is Spider-Man's real name?

8

Whose military defenses were called the Maginot Line?

9

What was known as the "Tin Lizzie"?

10

Which letter is to the right of B on a computer keyboard?

11

What is etymology?

12

What is the Jewish Day of Atonement also called?

GENERAL KNOWLEDGE
NUMBER 11

1

How many psalms are there in the Book of Psalms?

2

In which year did the *Titanic* sink?

3

Who was the Enlightened One?

4

If you are crapulous what are you?

5

Al Gore was the senator for which state?

6

Who narrated Jeff Wayne's "The War of the Worlds"?

7

Who wrote the novel *A Passage to India*?

8

In which Russian city is The State Hermitage Museum?

9

Name the eight countries that border France.

10

What can be a short jacket or a dance?

11

What is the cube root of 64?

12

Which US president's wife was named Rosalynn?

1

Who said: "There's a sucker born every minute"?

2

What is a moke?

3

Who sends encyclical letters?

4

Who in 1848 wrote *The Communist Manifesto*?

5

Where was the wheel supposedly invented?

6

Who played Max Bialystock in the original film *The Producers*?

7

Who wrote the theme music for the movie *Kill Bill*?

8

What is performed every ten years at Oberammergau?

9

What is a natterjack?

10

In the Bible, who first saw the writing on the wall?

11

What is *pâté de foie gras*?

12

What does a necrologist write?

1

What is pinchbeck?

2

Who said: "An army marches on its stomach"?

3

What animal does a *mahout* take care of?

4

How did Otis Reading die?

5

What is examined using an otoscope?

6

What is one third of one half?

7

Who wrote the novel *The Accidental Tourist*?

8

In the Chinese calendar which animal follows the sheep?

9

Parmentier means garnished or cooked with which vegetable?

10

Who composed the opera *Peter Grimes*?

11

Which movie star wrote a novel called *The Constant Sinner*?

12

Tony Curtis said of which co-star: "It was like kissing Hitler"?

GENERAL KNOWLEDGE
NUMBER 14

1

Alphabetically, what is the first creature in the dictionary?

2

By what two other names has St Petersburg been known?

3

At sea, how long is a dogwatch?

4

Among which larger group of islands are the Fox Islands?

5

What did Anton Drexler found in 1919?

6

What is the capital of Pakistan?

7

What does the Q stand for in IQ?

8

Whose catchphrase is "What's up, Doc?"?

9

What is the last letter of the modern Greek alphabet?

10

If your birthday is March 24, what star sign are you?

11

Which number is the current French Republic?

12

In which sport might you do a Triffus?

GENERAL KNOWLEDGE
NUMBER 15

1

Which country's currency is the dalasi?

2

Which Disney movie features the song "Topsy Turvy"?

3

In which city does the annual Oktoberfest take place?

4

Which is the sixth of the Ten Commandments?

5

How many pecks are there in a bushel?

6

They may be complex, vulgar or mixed—what are they?

7

What was U2's first album?

8

How many lines has a limerick?

9

Who is Jon Voight's songwriter brother?

10

Tariffs and quotas are used in which kind of war?

11

What do the initials stand for in J D Salinger?

12

What is the French stock exchange called?

1

Which French singer was called the "little sparrow"?

2

Name the controversial Salman Rushdie novel published in 1988.

3

What was Charlie Chaplin's first fully talking movie?

4

In Ireland, what is the prime minister called?

5

What word both means halo and cloud?

6

In which year was President Eisenhower inaugurated?

7

What color is the "black box" on an aircraft?

8

What was Greta Garbo's real name?

9

What is the name of the bobsled course at St Moritz?

10

Who wrote the play *The Misanthrope*?

11

How many faces does a tetrahedron have?

12

Ikebana is the Japanese art of what?

1

In which state is the Painted Desert?

2

What is the name of the dog in *Peter Pan*?

3

What is the principal ingredient in the Indian dish dahl?

4

Who was the UN Secretary-General killed in Africa in 1961?

5

Who was the great Athenian sculptor of the 5th century?

6

Name the character played by Mickey Rourke in *The Wrestler*.

7

What is the capital of Uruguay?

8

Of which country was Brian Boru king?

9

What part of an animal's body is its carapace?

10

Who is the author of the 19th-century novel *Dracula*?

11

How many strings does a balalaika have?

12

What is the Great Gatsby's first name?

GENERAL KNOWLEDGE
NUMBER 18

1

Which comet was visible during the Battle of Hastings in 1066?

2

Who was the UK prime minister during the First Gulf War?

3

In which 1980s movie does Julie Andrews take on a male role?

4

Which president's widow became a UN delegate?

5

In the Bible, who was King Ahab married to?

6

Which poet was a member of Oliver Cromwell's Council of State?

7

In which sport is nose riding a maneuver?

8

How many sides does a dodecagon have?

9

Who wrote the antiwar novel *All Quiet on the Western Front*?

10

What is the capital of Vietnam?

11

Who directed the movie *The Queen*?

12

Where do mice who are proverbially poor live?

GENERAL KNOWLEDGE
NUMBER 19

1

What does the distress call SOS stand for?

2

What item of headgear first appeared in London in 1797?

3

In which historic French building is the "Hall of Mirrors"?

4

Where is Charles Darwin buried?

5

Which tradesman would use a quern?

6

Who wrote *The Legend of Sleepy Hollow*?

7

Whose motto was "All for one, one for all"?

8

What is the Dutch liqueur made with eggs, sugar, and brandy?

9

Who did the Germans call *Der Bingle*?

10

Which football player was called "The Fridge"?

11

Which rap star remarried his ex-wife Kimberley in 2006?

12

Which two English poets jointly published *Lyrical Ballads* in 1798?

1

Who played the title role in the movie *Hans Christian Andersen*?

2

What do you call whipped cream flavored with vanilla?

3

Which flag is flown when a ship is about to sail?

4

What is the center of an atom called?

5

In which year did the IRA come into being?

6

What is the family's last name in Louisa May Alcott's *Little Women*?

7

What side of a ship is starboard, left or right?

8

What is the name of the artists' colony at Saratoga Springs, NY?

9

How many hours are there in two weeks?

10

In curling, the tee sits in the center of what?

11

Which English novelist won the Nobel Prize in 2007?

12

Who composed the music for *A Chorus Line*?

GENERAL KNOWLEDGE
NUMBER 21

1

What was Richard Burton's last movie?

2

How is the German Ardennes offensive of 1944 better known?

3

Which prima ballerina married a Panamanian diplomat in 1955?

4

Which city is known as "Beer Town"?

5

What rope is used for tying up a ship?

6

Which crab makes its home in another creature's shell?

7

In Greek mythology, which trio represented beauty?

8

Who is the patron saint of Venice?

9

Who is the "Eternal President" of North Korea?

10

Who plays Madonna's chauffeur in the video of her song "Music"?

11

Which vice-president couldn't spell "potato"?

12

Who invented the miners' safety lamp?

1

Semper Fidelis is the motto of which US fighting force?

2

Which Charles created the comic strip *Peanuts*?

3

Who was the Egyptian sun god?

4

Who wrote the book *The Magnificent Ambersons*?

5

Manama is the capital of which Middle Eastern country?

6

Who was the leading poet of the Beat Movement?

7

Which US writer created the genre of the western?

8

What color is a ship's quarantine flag?

9

In the TV series *Frasier*, who played Daphne Moon's father?

10

Which is the world's oldest existing city?

11

What do ichthyologists study?

12

In which region of Spain is Barcelona?

1

What do the Argentinians call the Falkland Islands?

2

Which barrel is larger, a butt or a hogshead?

3

Of which basketball team is Jack Nicholson an ardent supporter?

4

What are "spring" and "neap" types of?

5

Which Verdi opera had its premiere in Cairo in 1871?

6

What was the first bird released from Noah's Ark?

7

Who did Renate Blauel marry on Valentine's Day, 1984?

8

In whose stories was the "great grey-green greasy Limpopo River"?

9

Who wrote *The Decline and Fall of the Roman Empire*?

10

Which 12th-century band of knights protected pilgrims to the Holy Land?

11

What are Gold Murderer and Thunder & Lightning?

12

In which year was the first New York City Marathon staged?

1

What is a liana?

2

What is the last book in the New Testament?

3

What does the abbreviation GDP stand for?

4

Which art movement did Pablo Picasso and Georges Braque begin?

5

What are the top universities in the US known as?

6

Which is greater, 2/3rd or 7/10th?

7

The modern Russian alphabet stems from which ancient alphabet?

8

Who played the title role in *The Life and Death of Peter Sellers*?

9

Sir Kay, Sir Percivale, and Sir Mordred were all what?

10

In which sport would you wear an obi?

11

What color is a bloodstone?

12

In its original French, what does the word biscuit mean?

ANSWERS
ART & LITERATURE

. . . .

WORDS AND PICTURES (1)

. . . .

1. Charlotte; 2. Michelangelo; 3. Captain Nemo; 4. Frederic Remington;
5. Dog (poodle); 6. Ernest Hemingway; 7. The Louvre in Paris;
8. *The Return of the King*; 9. Terry Pratchett; 10. Joanne Kathleen;
11. *Casino Royale*; 12. *Dove*

CHILDREN'S BOOKS

. . . .

1. Dr Seuss; 2. John Tenniel; 3. *Treasure Island*; 4. *Harry Potter and
the Prisoner of Azkaban*; 5. Dr Dolittle; 6. Michael and John;
7. Big Friendly Giant; 8. L Frank Baum; 9. Wilbur the pig;
10. Flopsy, Mopsy, Cottontail; 11. *The Little Prince;*
12. Jacob and Wilhelm

MODERN ART

. . . .

1. Jackson Pollock; 2. 1973; 3. Guernica; 4. Andy Warhol;
5. Peter Blake; 6. The Stars and Stripes; 7. Edward Hopper;
8. Lucian Freud; 9. Spanish; 10. Ireland; 11. Sculpture;
12. Salvador Dali

POETS AND POETRY

. . . .

1. Sylvia Plath; 2. Samuel Taylor Coleridge;
3. Walt Whitman; 4. Paradise; 5. "Daffodils" by William Wordsworth;
6. Emily Dickinson; 7. Wystan Hugh; 8. Sylvia Plath's; 9. Nightingale;
10. "The Old Vicarage, Grantchester" by Rupert Brooke;
11. Bysshe; 12. Ogden Nash's

ANSWERS
ART & LITERATURE

FAMOUS PEN NAMES

1. Lewis Carroll; 2. John le Carré; 3. Mark Twain; 4. Dr Seuss;
5. Voltaire; 6. Gore Vidal; 7. O Henry; 8. George Orwell;
9. George Eliot; 10. Isak Dinesen; 11. Ellis Bell; 12. Ellery Queen

WORDS AND PICTURES (2)

1. John Steinbeck; 2. Camille Pissarro; 3. Alarm clock;
4. Jamie Wyeth; 5. Michael Crichton; 6. Pablo Picasso's;
7. 27; 8. Bilbo Baggins; 9. Douglas Adams; 10. Raffaello Santi;
11. Francis; 12. Auguste Rodin

THE WORLD OF CHARLES DICKENS

1. Portsmouth; 2. *The Mystery of Edwin Drood*; 3. *David Copperfield*;
4. Jack Dawkins; 5. Ellen Ternan; 6. London and Paris;
7. Sarah Gamp; 8. *Hard Times*; 9. Jacob Marley;
10. Marshalsea prison; 11. Wackford Squeers; 12. *Barnaby Rudge*

WHO PAINTED THESE?

1. Thomas Gainsborough; 2. Jan Vermeer; 3. Edgar Degas;
4. Michelangelo; 5. Gustav Klimt; 6. Leonardo da Vinci;
7. Edvard Munch; 8. Pierre-Auguste Renoir; 9. Claude Monet;
10. Vincent van Gogh; 11. Hieronymus Bosch;
12. Henri de Toulouse-Lautrec

ANSWERS
ART & LITERATURE

. . . .

CLASSIC CHARACTERS

. . . .

1. Athos, Porthos, Aramis; 2. The Hunchback of Notre Dame;
3. *Moby Dick;* 4. Emma; 5. *Sense and Sensibility*; 6. Sherlock Holmes;
7. Becky Sharp; 8. Rosinante; 9. *Crime and Punishment*;
10. Lemuel; 11. *The Scarlet Letter*; 12. Uncas

LITERARY SLEUTHS

. . . .

1. Dorothy L Sayers; 2. *The Big Sleep*; 3. Sherlock Holmes;
4. Nancy Drew; 5. C Auguste Dupin; 6. The 87th precinct;
7. Mike Hammer; 8. Australia; 9. Belgian; 10. Dashiell Hammett;
11. Ross Macdonald; 12. William of Baskerville

WORDS AND PICTURES (3)

. . . .

1. *Prix Goncourt*; 2. Madrid; 3. Canadian; 4. Casanova;
5. *Mona Lisa*; 6. Edith Wharton; 7. A maquette;
8. Ezra Pound; 9. Mural; 10. *Sense and Sensibility*;
11. Truman Capote's; 12. John James Audubon

WHO WROTE THESE NOVELS?

. . . .

1. J M Barrie; 2. Jane Austen; 3. Henry Fielding; 4. Peter Benchley;
5. William Thackeray; 6. Stieg Larsson; 7. Herman Melville;
8. H G Wells; 9. Alexandre Dumas; 10. Bram Stoker;
11. Gertrude Stein; 12. Stephen Crane

. . . .

ANSWERS
ART & LITERATURE

....

ARTISTS IN THE FRAME

....

1. Norman Rockwell; 2. (Sandro) Botticelli's; 3. Claude Monet;
4. Paul Gauguin; 5. Russia; 6. Raphael;
7. Henri de Toulouse-Lautrec; 8. Pablo Picasso's; 9. 15th;
10. Peter Paul Rubens; 11. El Greco; 12. James McNeill Whistler

....

ALL ABOUT THE BARD

....

1. Anne Hathaway; 2. Julius Caesar; 3. *The Taming of the Shrew*;
4. Trojan War; 5. *The Winter's Tale*; 6. Montague and Capulet;
7. *The Tempest*; 8. *Timon of Athens*; 9. St George's (23 April);
10. Forest of Arden; 11. Goneril, Regan, Cordelia; 12. Lucrece

....

WORDS AND PICTURES (4)

....

1. Nick Hornby's; 2. Prehistoric cave paintings; 3. Wigan Pier; 4. Three;
5. Dadaism; 6. Father; 7. F A Bartholdi;
8. Elizabeth, Jane, Mary, Lydia, Kitty; 9. Plato; 10. Captain Ahab;
11. Van Dyck (later Sir Anthony Vandyke);
12. Leo Tolstoy

....

MORE POETS AND POETRY

....

1. Henry Wadsworth Longfellow; 2. Robert Frost; 3. Thomas Stearns;
4. 14; 5. Maya Angelou; 6. Seamus Heaney;
7. John Keats; 8. "Funeral Blues"; 9. "The Star-Spangled Banner";
10. George; 11. Federico García Lorca; 12. Hart Crane

....

ANSWERS
ART & LITERATURE

PLAYS AND PLAYWRIGHTS

1. Harold Pinter; 2. T S Eliot; 3. Eugene O'Neill's; 4. *Pygmalion*;
5. *A Streetcar Named Desire*; 6. Sophocles; 7. Czechoslovakia;
8. Christopher Marlowe; 9. *The Vagina Monologues*;
10. George Bernard Shaw; 11. *The Crucible*; 12. Ireland

OLD MASTERS

1. Venice; 2. Goya; 3. Claude Monet; 4. Eight; 5. Christina Rossetti;
6. Vincent Van Gogh's; 7. Edouard Manet; 8. A clam shell;
9. Edgar Degas; 10. John Everett Millais; 11. 17th;
12. Jacques Louis David

FICTIONAL PLACES

1. Narnia; 2. Dr Doolittle; 3. *Gulliver's Travels*; 4. Airstrip One;
5. Ork;; 6. William Faulkner; 7. Peter Pan; 8. P G Wodehouse;
9. Garrison Keillor's; 10. *Lost Horizon*; 11. Maple White Land;
12. Dublin

20TH-CENTURY CLASSICS

1. Richard Adams; 2. *Rebecca* (Daphne du Maurier);
3. Mellors the gamekeeper; 4. Gunther Grass; 5. Humbert Humbert;
6. *Scoop*; 7. *Animal Farm*; 8. Lee Harvey Oswald; 9. *Catcher in the Rye*;
10. *For Whom the Bell Tolls*; 11. *A Clockwork Orange*; 12. Harper Lee's

ANSWERS
ART & LITERATURE

....

MORE MODERN ART

....

1. Damien Hirst's; 2. Russian; 3. Jeff Koons; 4. Mark Rothko;
5. 58; 6. Charles Saatchi; 7. Belgian; 8. Man Ray;
9. Flowers; 10. Yorkshire; 11. Roy Lichtenstein;
12. Bilbao

....

MORE CHILDREN'S BOOKS

....

1. Frog; 2. Ted Hughes; 3. Bear; 4. Maurice Sendak;
5. Psamead (sand fairy); 6. Pew; 7. *Madame Doubtfire*;
8. E B White's; 9. Veruca Salt; 10. Chimney-sweep; 11. Muggles;
12. *The Amber Spyglass*

....

WORDS AND PICTURES (5)

....

1. Henry James; 2. Hotel Chelsea; 3. South Africa;
4. Sir Walter Scott; 5. James Thurber; 6. London magistrate;
7. Lew Wallace; 8. *The Exorcist*; 9. *Carrie:* 10. The Turkey;
11. *The Maltese Falcon*; 12. Nathaniel Hawthorne

....

ANSWERS
MOVIES & TELEVISION

....

MOVIE TITLES (1): ADD THE NUMBERS

....

1. *12*; 2. *Three*; 3. *8*; 4. *Two*; 5. *13*; 6. *23*; 7. *Seven*;
8. *Nine*; 9. *92*; 10. *Six*; 11. *Five*; 12. *20,000*

....

TV SITCOMS

....

1. Geoffrey; 2. Winslow; 3. The Bronx; 4. Fisherman's hat;
5. Accountant and mailman; 6. Three; 7. Fort Baxter; 8. Dick Sargent;
9. *Till Death Us Do Part*; 10. Reverend Jim Ignatowski;
11. Carl Reiner; 12. Jay Leno

....

WHAT ARE THEIR "MOVIE STAR" NAMES?

....

1. Rock Hudson; 2. Charlton Heston; 3. Rita Hayworth;
4. Boris Karloff; 5. Whoopi Goldberg; 6. Kirk Douglas;
7. Lauren Bacall; 8. Alan Alda; 9. Ben Kingsley; 10. Fred Astaire;
11. Cher; 12. Stewart Granger

....

WESTERN MOVIES

....

1. Kirk Douglas; 2. *The Big Country*: 3. Sam Peckinpah; 4. *Stagecoach*;
5. Nat King Cole and Stubby Kaye; 6. James Stewart;
7. Annie Proulx's; 8. *Guns in the Afternoon*; 9. Steve McQueen;
10. Wyatt Earp; 11. Claudia Cardinale; 12. Marlon Brando

....

ANSWERS
MOVIES & TELEVISION

....

MULTISCREEN (1)

....

1. Barbara Hale; 2. Replicants; 3. *Julia;* 4. Christmas Day (1995);
5. 1975; 6. *Some Like It Hot*; 7. Donald Sutherland; 8. The Tates and
the Campbells; 9. Byron; 10. Jessica Fletcher (of *Murder, She Wrote*);
11. Daniel Day-Lewis; 12. *8 Mile*

TV CRIMEBUSTERS

....

1. David and Kenneth; 2. Stacy Keach; 3. Kojak; 4. Lt Philip Gerard;
5. Sgt. Phil Esterhaus; 6. Craig Stevens; 7. Las Vegas;
8. William Conrad; 9. David Caruso; 10. Ridley and Tony Scott;
11. Cynthia Gibb; 12. Joseph

FESTIVALS AND AWARDS

....

1. British Academy of Film and Television Arts; 2. 1928; 3. *True Grit;*
4. Hattie McDaniel (Best Supporting Actress for *Gone with the Wind*,
1939); 5. Golden Lion; 6. Daniel Day-Lewis;
7. George C Scott (for *Patton*); 8. *Erin Brockovich*;
9. *Terms of Endearment*; 10. Charles Chaplin (*The Circus*);
11. Robert Redford; 12. *The English Patient*

CRIME MOVIES

....

1. Donald Sutherland; 2. Ridley Scott; 3. *Heat*; 4. *Black Rain*;
5. Gwyneth Paltrow; 6. Woody Harrelson; 7. *Gumshoe*;
8. Buster Edwards; 9. Hell; 10. *The Long Goodbye*; 11. J J Gittes;
12. *The Boston Strangler*

....

ANSWERS
MOVIES & TELEVISION

. . . .

MAKE 'EM LAUGH

. . . .

1. Laurel and Hardy; 2. Roseanne Harris-Conner; 3. Dean Martin and Jerry Lewis; 4. Cheryl Hines; 5. *The Man With Two Brains*; 6. The Three Stooges; 7. *Seinfeld*; 8. Louie De Palma; 9. *These Friends of Mine*; 10. DuBois; 11. *Flight of the Conchords*; 12. Count Basie's

. . . .

MULTISCREEN (2)

. . . .

1. Boston Red Sox; 2. Joel and Ethan; 3. Allison Janney; 4. *Harry Potter and the Order of the Phoenix*; 5. Hollywood Foreign Press Association; 6. Japanese; 7. Columbia Broadcasting System; 8. Peter Jackson; 9. *Strictly Come Dancing*; 10. Chris Columbus; 11. *Toast of the Town*; 12. Cate Blanchett, Nicole Kidman, Russell Crowe, Geoffrey Rush

. . . .

JAMES BOND MOVIES

. . . .

1. *Dr No;* 2. Madonna; 3. They made seven movies each; 4. Timothy Dalton; 5. Sean Bean; 6. Australian; 7. His hat; 8. The role of Blofeld; 9. *Never Say Never Again*; 10. Desmond Llewelyn; 11. David Niven; 12. Sean Connery (32)

. . . .

MOVIE MUSICALS

. . . .

1. Tim Curry; 2. Sharks and Jets; 3. *The Philadelphia Story;* 4. Glynis Johns; 5. Cy Coleman; 6. Damon Runyon's; 7. *The Barkleys of Broadway*; 8. Jonathan Pryce; 9. Carol Reed; 10. *Singin' in the Rain;* 11. Gene Kelly; 12. John C Reilly

. . . .

ANSWERS
MOVIES & TELEVISION

....

ALTERNATIVE CAREERS OF THE STARS

....

1. Ghana and Czechoslovakia; 2. Julia Roberts; 3. Danny DeVito;
4. Robin Williams; 5. Clint Eastwood; 6. Melina Mercouri;
7. Cary Grant; 8. Sue Lyon; 9. Photo-journalism; 10. Veronica Lake;
11. Jane Russell; 12. Paul Newman

....

MOVIE TITLES (2): ADD THE PLACE NAMES

....

1. *Seattle*; 2. *Broadway*; 3. *Alaska*; 4. *Iwo Jima*; 5. *Java*; 6. *Baghdad*;
7. *Greenwich*; 8. *St Louis*; 9. *Hollywood*; 10. *Philadelphia*;
11. *Casablanca*; 12. *Tokyo*

....

CLINT EASTWOOD AND HIS MOVIES

....

1. .44 Magnum; 2. *Paint Your Wagon;* 3. William Munny;
4. *Play Misty for Me*; 5. *Absolute Power*; 6. Movie director John
Huston; 7. Rowdy Yates; 8. Mayor of Carmel; 9. James Garner, Donald
Sutherland, Tommy Lee Jones; 10. *Gran Torino*;
11. Chief Dan George; 12. Clint Eastwood, Lee Van Cleef, Eli Wallach

....

MULTISCREEN (3)

....

1. Virginia Woolf; 2. Ork; 3. Boston Red Sox;
4. *The Absent-Minded Professor;* 5. Elizabeth Taylor; 6. Barney Rubble;
7. James Cromwell; 8. Marion Michael Morrison;
9. Jonas Brothers; 10. Mrs Weasley; 11. Charlie Chaplin;
12. Damian Lewis

....

ANSWERS
MOVIES & TELEVISION

. . . .

ANIMALS ON SCREEN

. . . .

1. Ross in *Friends*; 2. White Persian; 3. Trigger; 4. Toto; 5. 72;
6. The Pie; 7. As Lassie; 8. Keiko the whale; 9. Moose and Enzo;
10. Spike; 11. German Shepherd; 12. Clyde

TV DRAMA

. . . .

1. Sterling Cooper; 2. Lady Jessica Montford; 3. Vice President;
4. Tony Kushner; 5. Vicodin; 6. St Gregory; 7. Gina Lollobrigida;
8. "Woke Up This Morning"; 9. Oahu; 10. Graem Bauer;
11. Kate O'Mara; 12. Joshua Rush

FAMILY CONNECTIONS

. . . .

1. Tippi Hedron; 2. First cousins; 3. Beau; 4. Suzy Kendall;
5. Frank Lloyd Wright; 6. Jonny Lee Miller; 7. Jack Nicholson;
8. Maureen O'Sullivan; 9. Michael Redgrave;
10. Margaux and Mariel Hemingway;
11. Keira Knightley; 12. Steve Forrest

WHOSE CATCHPHRASES WERE THESE?

. . . .

1. Steve McGarrett (*Hawaii Five-O*); 2. Jimmy Durante;
3. Homer Simpson (*The Simpsons*); 4. Ed McMahon (*The Tonight
Show*); 5. *Rowan & Martin's Laugh-In*; 6. Lt Kojak (*Kojak*);
7. Jack Benny; 8. Sgt Joe Friday (*Dragnet*);
9. Fred Flintstone (*The Flintstones*); 10. Lt Columbo (*Columbo*);
11. George Burns (*The Burns and Allen Show*); 12. Walter Cronkite

ANSWERS
MOVIES & TELEVISION

··

ALFRED HITCHCOCK MOVIES

··

1. Daphne du Maurier's; 2. Martin Balsam;
3. Charles Laughton and Elsa Lanchester;
4. *The Man Who Knew Too Much;* 5. Photographer; 6. Salvador Dali;
7. *Under Capricorn;* 8. Robert Donat; 9. The Cricket Test score;
10. A baby; 11. Mount Rushmore; 12. *Family Plot*

MULTISCREEN (4)

··

1. *The Long Good Friday;* 2. Dalton Trumbo;
3. Kim Basinger and Alec Baldwin; 4. David Fincher;
5. Dr Bunsen Honeydew; 6. Judi Dench's in *Shakespeare in Love;*
7. Sean Connery; 8. *Man About the House;*
9. Wanda in *A Fish Called Wanda;* 10. *Palme d'Or;* 11. Belgium;
12. Viggo Mortensen

ANSWERS
GEOGRAPHY

....

GLOBETROTTING (1)
....

1. Zurich; 2. Costa Rica; 3. Alluvium; 4. China; 5. Urdu;
6. Ecuador; 7. Portugal; 8. Mediterranean; 9. Simón Bolivar;
10. Argentina; 11. Neva; 12. Piraeus

....

ROLLING RIVERS
....

1. Yangtze; 2. South China Sea; 3. Zambezi; 4. Isar; 5. Loire;
6. Warsaw; 7. Dead Sea; 8. Burundi; 9. Ganges; 10. Red River;
11. Mackenzie; 12. Swan

....

MOUNTAINS HIGH
....

1. Pyrenees; 2. The Rockies; 3. Kilimanjaro; 4. New Zealand;
5. Mt Vinson; 6. Italy; 7. Mt Pico (Pico Island); 8. Mt Elbrus;
9. The Andes; 10. China and Nepal; 11. Mt Mitchell; 12. Australia

....

HOW WERE THESE PREVIOUSLY KNOWN? (1)
....

1. Ceylon; 2. Nyasaland; 3. British Honduras; 4. East Pakistan;
5. Siam; 6. Persia; 7. Zaire; 8. New Spain; 9. Gold Coast;
10. Gilbert Islands; 11. Abyssinia; 12. French Sudan

....

ANSWERS
GEOGRAPHY

....

GLOBETROTTING (2)

....

1. Delaware; 2. Italy; 3. Gulf of Mexico; 4. French; 5. Taipei;
6. Monaco; 7. Granada; 8. Adelaide; 9. Mt Fujiyama;
10. Zambezi; 11. Maine; 12. Malta, Gozo, Comino

WAVING THE FLAG

....

1. Canada's; 2. Red and white; 3. The 13 original colonies;
4. Five; 5. Vertical; 6. Commonwealth Star; 7. Black, red, yellow;
8. Crescent and star; 9. Japan's; 10. Isle of Man's;
11. Green, white, red; 12. 12

ISLANDS OF THE SEA

....

1. Denmark; 2. Scotland; 3. Vancouver Island; 4. South; 5. Dodecanese;
6. Southern Ocean; 7. Nauru; 8. Nine; 9. Borneo; 10. Cook Islands;
11. Chile; 12. Honshu

LAKES AND LOCHS

....

1. Italy; 2. Lake Ontario; 3. Bolivia and Peru; 4. Lake Baikal (Russia);
5. Florida; 6. North Island; 7. France; 8. Sierra Nevada;
9. Michigan, New York, Ohio, Pennsylvania; 10. Caspian Sea;
11. Northwest Territories; 12. Lake Eyre

ANSWERS
GEOGRAPHY

. . . .

LANDMARKS AND MONUMENTS

. . . .

1. Agra; 2. Tunisia; 3. Ponte Vecchio; 4. Georgia; 5. George Washington, Thomas Jefferson, Theodore Roosevelt, Abraham Lincoln; 6. Rotorua; 7. Northern Ireland; 8. Ayers Rock; 9. Giza; 10. Switzerland; 11. Red Square (Moscow); 12. Peru

GLOBETROTTING (3)

. . . .

1. Knesset; 2. Amazon; 3. Tallinn; 4. Venezuela; 5. Belgium, France, Germany; 6. Yellowstone; 7. Grand Canal of China; 8. Danube; 9. Washington DC; 10. France; 11. The Urals; 12. Rome

COMING TO TERMS

. . . .

1. Western; 2. Nautical mile; 3. Northern; 4. Confluence; 5. Strength of earthquakes; 6. Mesa; 7. Large waterfall; 8. Archipelago; 9. Lagoon; 10. The study of regional geography; 11. Magma; 12. Valley or ravine

SEAS AND OCEANS

. . . .

1. Pacific; 2. Australia and Tasmania; 3. Canada (Bay of Fundy); 4. Dead Sea; 5. Arctic; 6. Strait of Gibraltar; 7. Barents Sea; 8. Coral Sea; 9. Persian Gulf and Gulf of Oman; 10. Pacific; 11. Strait of Magellan; 12. Tyrrhenian Sea

ANSWERS
GEOGRAPHY

....

DESERT LANDSCAPES

....

1. Australia; 2. Atlas Mountains; 3. Thar Desert; 4. Antarctica;
5. Mongolia and China; 6. California; 7. 90%;
8. Botswana and Namibia; 9. Atacama Desert (Chile);
10. Western Australia; 11. Mojave (USA); 12. Takla Makan

....

CAPITAL CITIES

....

1. Berlin; 2. Salisbury; 3. Tallahassee; 4. Slovakia;
5. Wellington (NZ); 6. Asunción; 7. Reykjavik (Iceland); 8. Regina;
9. Bismarck; 10. Dublin; 11. Kigali; 12. La Paz (Bolivia)

....

GLOBETROTTING (4)

....

1. Nicaragua; 2. Acadia (Maine); 3. Quito; 4. Denmark and Sweden;
5. Yalta; 6. Oregon; 7. Spice Islands; 8. South Africa; 9. The Orkneys;
10. Fremantle; 11. Elbe; 12. Madrid

....

NAME THEIR CURRENCY

....

1. Rand; 2. Dong; 3. Shekel; 4. Cuban peso; 5. Egyptian pound;
6. Yuan Renmimbi; 7. Rouble; 8. Won; 9. Swiss franc; 10. Real;
11. Danish krone; 12. Tögrög or tugrik

....

ANSWERS
GEOGRAPHY

....

AIRPORTS OF THE WORLD

....

1. O'Hare; 2. Amsterdam; 3. Idlewild: 4. Glasgow; 5. Rome's;
6. Chek Lap Kok; 7. Sydney; 8. Heathrow; 9. Marco Polo; 10. Mumbai;
11. Montréal-Trudeau (Pierre Trudeau); 12. Tokyo

....

HOW WERE THESE PREVIOUSLY KNOWN? (2)

....

1. Peking; 2. Danzig; 3. Saigon; 4. New Amsterdam; 5. Dacca;
6. Kristiania; 7. Lourenço Marques; 8. Constantinople; 9. Gorky;
10. Edo; 11. Bombay; 12. Leopoldville

....

STATES WISE

....

1. Alabama; 2. California (Death Valley); 3. Delaware;
4. North Carolina; 5. Montana; 6. Minnesota; 7. Alaska; 8. Nebraska;
9. Washington; 10. Oklahoma; 11. Oregon; 12. Missouri

....

GLOBETROTTING (5)

....

1. Houston; 2. Corfu; 3. Canada; 4. Trimontaine;
5. Tigris and Euphrates; 6. Seven; 7. Libya; 8. Romania;
9. Luzon; 10. Mt Logan; 11. Murmansk; 12. Mali

....

ANSWERS
HISTORY

....

WAR AND PEACE
....

1. Eight; 2. Korean War; 3. Battle of Little Big Horn;
4. Britain and Spain; 5. War of American Independence; 6. France;
7. Japan; 8. Iran-Iraqi; 9. 116 years; 10. 1919; 11. American Civil War;
12. Athens and Sparta

....

WORLD WAR I
....

1. Archduke Franz Ferdinand's; 2. In taxis; 3. Belgium; 4. Ambulance
driver; 5. Tank; 6. Siegfried Sassoon; 7. Australia and New Zealand;
8. Netherlands; 9. Second battle of Ypres; 10. General John Pershing;
11. Field Marshal Douglas Haig: 12. Rank and file of the 1914 British
Expeditionary Force

....

WHO SAID THAT?
....

1. Henry Ford; 2. Karl Marx; 3. Oscar Wilde; 4. Adolf Hitler;
5. Charles De Gaulle; 6. Richard Nixon; 7. Abraham Lincoln;
8. President Harry S Truman; 9. Adlai Stevenson; 10. Elizabeth I;
11. Ronald Reagan; 12. Israeli Defense Minister Moshe Dayan

....

PAST TIMES (1)
....

1. Ireland; 2. New York City Subway; 3. Flatiron Building in
New York; 4. Babylon; 5. The Commonwealth of England (1649-60);
6. Inca; 7. Winston Churchill; 8. 33 days; 9. By suicide with a cyanide
capsule; 10. 63 (and seven months); 11. The YMCA; 12. 1975

....

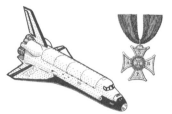   

ANSWERS
HISTORY

....

YEARS TO REMEMBER

....

1.1917; 2.1949; 3.1666; 4.1959; 5.1979; 6.1967; 7.1988; 8.1989; 9.1773;
10. 1990; 11.1987; 12.1948

....

KINGS AND QUEENS

....

1. Denmark; 2. Nicholas II; 3. Juliana; 4. Louis XVI;
5. Two; 6. Umberto II; 7. Albania; 8. Austrian; 9. Napoleon II;
10. King Farouk; 11. Ibn Saud; 12. Emperor Hirohito

....

THE CIVIL WAR

....

1. Alexander Stephens; 2. Vicksburg; 3. Tennessee; 4. General "Jeb"
Stuart; 5. General George Meade; 6. William Seward;
7. Albert Sidney Johnston and Joseph E Johnston; 8. *Monitor*;
9. Andersonville; 10. Tecumseh; 11. Lew Wallace; 12. Mathew Brady's

....

THE 1960s

....

1. 1961; 2. John Glenn; 3. The Warren Commission's; 4. Gary Powers;
5. Rachel Carson's; 6. Malcolm X; 7. Pope Paul VI; 8. Felt-tip pen;
9. Prague Spring; 10. Golda Meir; 11. Boeing 747; 12. Bolivia

....

HOW WERE THESE BETTER KNOWN?

....

1. Lenin; 2. The Red Baron; 3. Malcolm X; 4. La Pasionaria;
5. Buddha; 6. Lawrence of Arabia; 7. Mother Teresa; 8. El Cid;
9. Gerald Ford; 10. Leon Trotsky; 11. Pol Pot; 12. Tito

ANSWERS
HISTORY

PAST TIMES (2)

1. 1904; 2. Thomas Paine; 3. William Bligh; 4. Geronimo;
5. Rajiv Gandhi; 6. 1933; 7. Amelia Earhart; 8. Mary Baker Eddy;
9. Hungary; 10. William "Boss" Tweed; 11. Pat Garrett; 12. Dutch

WHICH COUNTRY?

1. France; 2. Cambodia; 3. Greece; 4. Spain; 5. Rwanda; 6. Prussia;
7. Czechoslovakia; 8. Germany; 9. Finland; 10. Ceylon; 11. England;
12. Vietnam

PAST TIMES (3)

1. An Englishman named Edward Teach; 2. Trygve Lie;
3. Charles Darwin; 4. Alaska; 5. Adrian IV; 6. Robert E Lee's;
7. The Althing in Iceland; 8. 17th; 9. Cleveland, Ohio; 10. Anastasia;
11. Tasmania; 12. 1863

THE 1970s

1. Salvador Allende; 2. Cigarette advertising; 3. Richard Nixon;
4. A knighthood; 5. Mother Teresa; 6. Spiro Agnew; 7. 19; 8. 1973;
9. Patricia Hearst; 10. Idi Amin; 11. Jerry Brown; 12. Rev Jim Jones

MORE YEARS TO REMEMBER

1. 1914; 2. 1947; 3. 1968; 4. 1916; 5. 2003; 6. 1865; 7. 1947; 8. 1849;
9. 1837; 10. 1962; 11. 1886; 12. 1854

ANSWERS
HISTORY

MILITARY MEN

1. Napoleon and Wellington; 2. The Carthaginian; 3. General Lafayette; 4. Hernán Cortés; 5. General Norman Schwarzkopf; 6. Paul von Hindenburg; 7. Saladin; 8. Ulysses Simpson Grant; 9. Admiral Ernest King; 10. Marshal Zhukov; 11. General Maxwell D Taylor; 12. General James Wolfe

PRESIDENTS OF THE UNITED STATES

1. Milhous; 2. Herbert Hoover; 3. James Garfield; 4. George Clinton; 5. Zachary Taylor; 6. James Buchanan; 7. Woodrow Wilson; 8. William Henry Harrison; 9. Andrew Jackson; 10. Benjamin Harrison; 11. John Adams and Thomas Jefferson; 12. George B McClellan

FAMOUS EXPLORERS

1. *Golden Hind*; 2. Sally Ride; 3. Ferdinand Magellan; 4. Vivian Fuchs; 5. Australia; 6. Vasco da Gama; 7. Wales; 8. Marco Polo; 9. Reaching the summit of Mt Everest; 10. Richard Burton; 11. The Niger; 12. Amerigo Vespucci

NICKNAMES

1. Duke of Wellington; 2. Ronald Reagan; 3. Attila the Hun; 4. President François Duvalier of Haiti; 5. Napoleon Bonaparte; 6. General Erwin Rommel; 7. Margaret Thatcher; 8. General George S Patton; 9. President Nicolas Sarkozy; 10. Otto von Bismarck; 11. Louis XIV of France; 12. Former Panamanian president Manuel Noriega

ANSWERS
HISTORY

....

THE 1980s

....

1. Columbia; 2. Iranian; 3. Mark Chapman; 4. Its bicentenary;
5. The tanker *Exxon Valdez*; 6. 1986; 7. Kurt Waldheim;
8. Michael Dukakis; 9. Grenada; 10. François Mitterrand;
11. Ronald Reagan; 12. Indira Gandhi

....

WORLD WAR II

....

1. German invasion of Russia; 2. V-J Day;
3. Admiral Karl Dönitz; 4. 1942; 5. General Bernard Montgomery;
6. Rudolf Hess; 7. French Resistance; 8. Omaha and Utah;
9. USS *Missouri*; 10. Tehran; 11. Marshal Pétain; 12. 56

....

ANCIENT WORLD

....

1. Helen of Troy's; 2. Caligula; 3. Cyrus the Great; 4. Athens;
5. Emperor Hadrian; 6. Vulcan; 7. Macedonia; 8. Spartacus;
9. By drinking hemlock; 10. Julius Caesar; 11. Persians and Greeks;
12. Cicero

....

PAST TIMES (4)

....

1. Buffalo, NY; 2. Benito Mussolini's; 3. Tutankhamun's tomb;
4. Brazil; 5. General Ambrose Burnside (who prominently sported
them); 6. Charles II; 7. 14th; 8. Wiley Post; 9. Australia;
10. Kemal Atatürk; 11. Ming; 12. Pigeon post

....

ANSWERS
MUSIC

....

NAME THE LEADER OF THE BAND

....

1. Ginger Baker; 2. Brian Wilson; 3. Diana Ross; 4. Clyde McPhatter;
5. Otis Williams; 6. Frankie Valli; 7. Levi Stubbs; 8. Ray Davies;
9. Roger Daltry; 10. Jim Morrison; 11. Jerry Garcia; 12. Robert Plant

....

WHO DID THEY BECOME?

....

1. George Michael; 2. Barry Manilow; 3. Patsy Cline; 4. Bo Diddley;
5. Snoop Doggy Dogg; 6. Chaka Khan; 7. Tina Turner; 8. Meat Loaf;
9. David Bowie; 10. Cat Stevens (then Yusef Islam);
11. Procol Harum; 12. Irving Berlin

....

THE BEATLES

....

1. The Quarrymen; 2. Decca; 3. Julian Lennon;
4. Paul McCartney and Ringo Starr; 5. Paul McCartney; 6. "Michelle";
7. Jesus; 8. Peter Sellers; 9. Beatles' manager Brian Epstein;
10. Paul McCartney; 11. *The Ed Sullivan Show*;
12. "The Long And Winding Road"

....

WHICH POP GROUPS ARE THESE?

....

1. The Three Degrees; 2. The Four Aces; 3. The Ronettes;
4. The Eurythmics; 5. The Four Tops; 6. Cream;
7. Pet Shop Boys; 8. The Supremes; 9. Aerosmith; 10. R.E.M.;
11. Led Zeppelin; 12. Peter, Paul and Mary

....

ANSWERS
MUSIC

....

POP GOES THE 60s

....

1. "Nut Rocker"; 2. "Monday, Monday"; 3. Don; 4. Glen Campbell;
5. "(I Can't Get No) Satisfaction"; 6. 1967; 7. Bobby Vee's; 8. Stevie
Wonder; 9. Richard Harris; 10. Carl Wilson; 11. Shangri-Las;
12. Frank and Nancy Sinatra

....

MUSICAL MEDLEY (1)

....

1. Wink Martindale ("Deck of Cards"); 2. James; 3. Che Guevara;
4. Five; 5. The Bolshoi; 6. Simon and Garfunkel's; 7. His sense of smell;
8. Annie Lennox; 9. Marian Anderson; 10. Rod Stewart;
11. Donny Osmond; 12. Aretha Franklin

....

BROADWAY MUSICALS

....

1. *The Sound of Music*; 2. *Man of La Mancha*; 3. T S Eliot's;
4. *Pal Joey*; 5. Jim Dale; 6. "Stranger in Paradise"; 7. John McMartin;
8. Stephen Sondheim; 9. *The Phantom of the Opera*;
10. Alexander Borodin's; 11. *A Chorus Line*; 12. *Guys and Dolls*

....

COLOR THESE SONGS

....

1. Yellow; 2. Black; 3. Orange; 4. Indigo; 5. Scarlet; 6. Pink; 7. Yellow;
8. Purple; 9. Green; 10. Pink; 11. Blue; 12. Gold

....

POP GOES THE 70s

....

1. Nancy Spungen; 2. 10cc; 3. "Breaking Up Is Hard To Do"; 4. David
Cassidy; 5. 27; 6. "Got To Be There"; 7. The Ramones; 8. Linda Ronstadt;
9. Donny Osmond; 10. 1977; 11. Nine; 12. Warren Beatty

....

ANSWERS
MUSIC

....

MUSICAL MEDLEY (2)

....

1. The Crickets; 2. John Michael Osbourne; 3. "Abbey Road";
4. Amsterdam; 5. Tex Ritter; 6. Carole King's; 7. Trombone;
8. Florenz Ziegfeld's; 9. *Dick Tracy*; 10. *Slumdog Millionaire*;
11. Winston; 12. W S Gilbert

....

ALL THAT JAZZ

....

1. Django Reinhardt; 2. Cornet; 3. Joe "King" Oliver; 4. Glenn Miller;
5. Bessie Smith; 6. Satchmo (Louis Armstrong); 7. Benny Goodman;
8. Billie Holiday; 9. Duke Ellington, Earl Hines, Count Basie;
10. Buddy Rich; 11. Canada; 12. *Jazz on a Summer's Day*

....

UNDER THE BATON

....

1. André Previn; 2. Arthur Fiedler; 3. Leopold Stokowski;
4. Philadelphia; 5. Chicago Symphony; 6. Sir Thomas Beecham;
7. Dutch; 8. Herbert von Karajan; 9. Arturo Toscanini;
10. Leonard Bernstein; 11. Arturo Toscanini; 12. Sir Simon Rattle

....

POP GOES THE 80S

....

1. Prince's; 2. Irene Cara; 3. Wham! (1985); 4. 1982; 5. 1981;
6. *Moonstruck*; 7. (Sir) Bob Geldof; 8. Madonna; 9. Christie Brinkley;
10. "Nebraska"; 11. "The Loco-Motion"; 12. "The Joshua Tree"

....

ANSWERS
MUSIC

....

101
MUSICAL MEDLEY (3)

....

1. Canada; 2. Saxophone; 3. Sergei Prokofiev; 4. Tim Rice;
5. Empty orchestra; 6. The Police; 7. *Holiday Inn;* 8. Cole Porter;
9. "When A Child Is Born"; 10. June Carter; 11. Arthur Sullivan;
12. Katherine Jenkins and Darcey Bussell

....

102
MUSIC FROM THE MOVIES

....

1. John Williams; 2. Zither; 3. *The Thomas Crown Affair* (original);
4. Dario Marianelli; 5. Clint Eastwood; 6. Gladys Knight;
7. "The Colonel Bogey March"; 8. Scott Joplin's; 9. Vangelis;
10. *An Inconvenient Truth;* 11. Max Steiner; 12. Maurice Jarre

....

103
GRAND OPERA

....

1. Gioacchino Rossini; 2. Milan La Scala; 3. Four;
4. Major female singer; 5. Jacques Offenbach; 6. William Schwenck;
7. Madame Butterfly; 8. *Billy Budd;* 9. Opera singer; 10. Libretto;
11. Joan Sutherland; 12. *Otello* and *Falstaff*

....

104
WHO COMPOSED THESE CLASSICS?

....

1. Sergei Prokofiev; 2. Camille Saint-Saëns; 3. Benjamin Britten;
4. George Frederic Handel; 5. Maurice Ravel; 6. Aaron Copland;
7. Claude Debussy; 8. Edward Elgar; 9. John Philip Sousa;
10. Johannes Brahms; 11. Jean Sibelius; 12. Frederick Delius

....

ANSWERS
MUSIC

POP GOES THE 90s

1. Hanson; 2. Prince; 3. Radiohead; 4. Manchester; 5. Linda Ronstadt and Aaron Neville; 6. Michael Jackson; 7. Sting; 8. The Monkees; 9. *Four Weddings and a Funeral*; 10. Rita Coolidge; 11. Sheryl Crow; 12. "Diva"

MUSICAL MEDLEY (4)

1. Léo Delibes; 2. Ravi Shankar; 3. Moon River; 4. "Kontiki"; 5. Belgian; 6. Bernie Taupin; 7. Mary Martin; 8. The Beastie Boys; 9. Micky Dolenz; 10. *Kid Galahad;* 11. Nigel Kennedy; 12. New Zealand

CLASSICAL NUMBERS

1. The Emperor; 2. Joseph Haydn; 3. Antonio Vivaldi; 4. Nine; 5. 20; 6. No 2; 7. 88; 8. Seven; 9. 35; 10. No 5; 11. Five; 12. Napoleon's retreat from Moscow

ROCK ON

1. Suzi Quatro; 2. Robert Plant; 3. Brian Jones; 4. *Love Me Tender*; 5. Little Richard; 6. B-52s; 7. George Michael's; 8. Bob Marley; 9. Buffalo Springfield; 10. David Bowie; 11. "Relax"; 12. Woodstock

MUSICAL MEDLEY (5)

1. Cher's; 2. Paris; 3. Harlem; 4. Elmer Bernstein; 5. Sir Lancelot; 6. "Happy Birthday To You"; 7. Suzi Quatro's; 8. Violin; 9. Peter Gabriel; 10. Victor Borge; 11. Matt Monro; 12. Richard Clayderman

ANSWERS
PEOPLE

110 ALL SORTS (1)

1. James Baldwin; 2. Thomas Edison; 3. Salvatori Lombino;
4. Dr Andrei Sakharov; 5. George Bernard Shaw; 6. James Madison;
7. Parker and Barrow; 8. Marion Davies; 9. Neapolitan (Italian);
10. Roald Amundsen; 11. Legal; 12. Edward Estlin

111 WHICH GEORGE?

1. George Michael; 2. George Bernard Shaw; 3. George III;
4. George Shearing; 5. George MacDonald Fraser; 6. George Burns;
7. George Armstrong Custer; 8. George Gershwin; 9. George Lucas;
10. George Marshall; 11. George Stevens; 12. George Wallace

112 CELEBRITY COUPLES

1. Richard Burton and Elizabeth Taylor; 2. Verona; 3. Skibo;
4. George S Kaufman and Moss Hart; 5. Queen Elizabeth and Prince
Philip; 6. Stan Laurel; 7. Beatrice; 8. Catherine Zeta-Jones and
Michael Douglas; 9. 1975; 10. John Gregory Dunne; 11. Dick and Tom;
12. Liza Minnelli

113 FAMOUS FIRSTS

1. Charles Lindbergh; 2. L Douglas Wilder (Virginia);
3. Peter Sellers; 4. Queen Victoria; 5. Valentina Tereshkova;
6. David Ben-Gurion; 7. Alexander Graham Bell;
8. Franklin Winfield Woolworth; 9. Virginia Dare; 10. Nancy Pelosi;
11. Joshua Slocum; 12. Captain Matthew Webb

ANSWERS
PEOPLE

WIVES OF PRESIDENTS

1. Raisa; 2. Martha Washington; 3. Carla Bruni; 4. Harry S Truman's; 5. Imelda Marcos; 6. Winnie Mandela; 7. Lady Bird Johnson; 8. Eva Perón; 9. James Madison's; 10. Betty Ford; 11. Elena Ceauşescu; 12. Eleanor Roosevelt

ALL SORTS (2)

1. Lenny Bruce; 2. Zechariah; 3. General "Billy" Mitchell; 4. Julia Ward Howe; 5. David Dwight Eisenhower; 6. Clarence Birdseye; 7. Douglas (Noel) Adams; 8. Howard Hughes; 9. General Mark Clark; 10. Standard Oil; 11. J D Salinger; 12. René Descartes

WHOSE LAST WORDS WERE THESE?

1. Elizabeth I; 2. Humphrey Bogart; 3. Anna Pavlova; 4. Charles Foster Kane in *Citizen Kane*; 5. Heinrich Heine; 6. Karl Marx; 7. Emperor Caligula; 8. Phineas T Barnum; 9. Lou Costello; 10. Ludwig van Beethoven; 11. Bing Crosby; 12. Hamlet

HEROES AND HEROINES

1. Admiral Horatio Nelson; 2. John McCain; 3. Audie Murphy; 4. Frederick Douglass; 5. Scotland; 6. Geronimo's; 7. Florence Nightingale; 8. Emiliano Zapata; 9. Malta; 10. Paul Revere; 11. Rosa Parks; 12. Captain Robert Falcon Scott

ANSWERS
PEOPLE

118

WHICH JOHN?

1. Johnny Cash; 2. John Wilkes Booth; 3. Johnny Depp;
4. John Updike; 5. John Cassavetes; 6. King John; 7. John Coltrane;
8. John Williams; 9. John Denver; 10. John Mills;
11. John Maynard Keynes; 12. John Dillinger

119

ALL SORTS (3)

1. Elizabeth Barrett and Robert Browning; 2. American;
3. Ivan the Terrible (Ivan IV); 4. Langhorne; 5. Paul McCartney;
6. Madeleine Albright; 7. Branwell Brontë; 8. Princess Anne;
9. Margaret Drabble; 10. Alexander Pope; 11. Richard Attenborough;
12. Erskine Caldwell

120

WHO DID THESE BECOME?

1. Pope Benedict XVI; 2. Bill Clinton; 3. Ho Chi Minh; 4. Elvis Costello;
5. Buffalo Bill; 6. Omar Sharif; 7. Joseph Stalin; 8. Julie Andrews;
9. Confucius; 10. Calamity Jane; 11. Bill Wyman; 12. Meg Ryan

121

CRIME ON THEIR MIND

1. Jack Ruby; 2. "Baby Face" Nelson; 3. Timothy McVeigh;
4. David Berkowitz; 5. James Earl Ray; 6. Piracy;
7. Carlos the Jackal; 8. Income-tax evasion; 9. Jack the Ripper;
10. Henri Charrière's (Papillon); 11. Zodiac Killer (he was never
caught); 12. Ronald Reagan

ANSWERS
PEOPLE

HOME SWEET HOME

1. Balmoral Castle; 2. Berchtesgaden; 3. Kykuit; 4. The Brontës;
5. Elysée Palace; 6. William Faulkner's; 7. James A Garfield;
8. Camp David; 9. L Frank Baum; 10. Richard Nixon's;
11. Ian Fleming's; 12. The British Chancellor of the Exchequer

ALL SORTS (4)

1. W C Field's; 2. Tom Wolfe; 3. Bobby Fischer; 4. Chicago;
5. Ambrose Bierce; 6. Andy Warhol; 7. Edmund Muskie; 8. Lawyer;
9. Czechoslovakia; 10. Florence Griffith-Joyner;
11. Cambodia; 12. Russia

SHOWBIZ SIBLINGS: ADD THE SURNAME

1. Baldwin; 2. Affleck; 3. Andrews; 4. Wahlberg; 5. Gyllenhaal;
6. Carradine; 7. Roberts; 8. Belushi; 9. Arquette; 10. Cusack;
11. Fonda; 12. Wilson

WHOSE NICKNAMES?

1. Ernest Hemingway; 2. Queen Mary I; 3. Muhammad Ali;
4. Frank Sinatra; 5. Jesse Owens; 6. Edith Piaf; 7. Thomas Edison;
8. William H Bonney; 9. Sarah Bernhardt;
10. Tony Blair; 11. Sylvester Stallone; 12. Imelda Marcos

ANSWERS
PEOPLE

....

WHAT A SCANDAL!

....

1. Robert Maxwell; 2. Linda Tripp; 3. Boris Becker; 4. Robert Mitchum;
5. Jimmy Swaggart; 6. Naomi Campbell; 7. Donna Rice;
8. Lana Turner's; 9. California's list of top tax evaders;
10. Martha Stewart; 11. Virginia Rappe; 12. Perjury

ALL SORTS (5)

....

1. Orville and Wilbur; 2. 2000; 3. St Jude; 4. Oliver Reed;
5. William Burroughs; 6. Elwyn Brooks; 7. The Artful Dodger;
8. Marilyn Monroe; 9. Franz Joseph Haydn; 10. Lech Wałęsa;
11. *The Tailor of Panama*; 12. George Bush

WHO SAID THESE?

....

1. George W Bush; 2. Groucho Marx; 3. Harold Macmillan;
4. Gerald Ford; 5. John Lennon; 6. Woody Allen; 7. Charles De Gaulle;
8. Richard Nixon; 9. Adolf Hitler; 10. Samuel Goldwyn;
11. Henry Kissinger; 12. Margaret Thatcher

WHICH HENRY?

....

1. Henry Hudson; 2. Henry Kissinger; 3. Henry V; 4. Henry Mancini;
5. Henry Miller; 6. Henry King; 7. Henry Clay; 8. Henry James;
9. Henry Cabot Lodge Jr; 10. Henry David Thoreau; 11. Henry Adams;
12. Henry VIII

ANSWERS
PEOPLE

130 — THE IMMORTALS

1. Narcissus; 2. Apollo; 3. 12; 4. Prometheus; 5. Poseidon; 6. Thor;
7. Golden apple; 8. Odysseus (or Ulysses); 9. Charon; 10. Bastet;
11. Midas; 12. Hermes

131 — ALL SORTS (6)

1. John Brown's; 2. Sir Edmund Hillary; 3. Patrick O'Brian's;
4. Huey Long; 5. Pearl Buck; 6. Ireland;
7. Lord Baden-Powell; 8. Anthony Shaffer;
9. Angela Merkel; 10. Keith; 11. Joan Collins;
12. Dorothy Parker

ANSWERS
SCIENCE & NATURE

···

RANDOM SAMPLE (1)

···

1. Brassica; 2. Lodge; 3. Smell; 4. Trepanning; 5. Radioactivity;
6. Watercress; 7. Cow (*vacca*); 8. Ozone; 9. Dog (called Laika);
10. Study of glands; 11. Pig; 12. Penguin

···

PLANTS AND TREES

···

1. Deadly Nightshade; 2. Cucumber; 3. Snakewood; 4. Giant Sequoia;
5. Stamen; 6. Three; 7. Algae; 8. Poppy; 9. Coconut;
10. Venus Fly Trap; 11. Yeast; 12. Underground

···

AMONG THE ANIMALS

···

1. Grasshopper; 2. Hair; 3. Bottom of sea or lake; 4. Polar;
5. Webbed; 6. Fox; 7. Sett; 8. Koala; 9. Hummingbird;
10. Male donkey and female horse; 11. Spiders; 12. Beetle

···

IDENTIFY THE MISSING COLLECTIVE NAMES

···

1. Dolphins; 2. Toads; 3. Piglets; 4. Budgies; 5. Tigers;
6. Giraffes; 7. Locusts; 8. Jellyfish; 9. Cats; 10. Pheasants;
11. Rhinoceros; 12. Magpies

···

THE HUMAN BODY

···

1. Femur (thighbone); 2. Neck; 3. Four; 4. Ear; 5. Kidneys; 6. 46;
7. Rapid Eye Movement; 8. Both have 24; 9. Right; 10. Skin;
11. Gristle; 12. Pancreas

···

ANSWERS
SCIENCE & NATURE

RANDOM SAMPLE (2)

1. Joseph Black; 2. Whip-poor-will; 3. Mulberry leaves;
4. Gene Cernan (Apollo 17, 1972); 5. Bee hummingbird; 6. Pink;
7. Irish Moss; 8. Large Hadron Collider (LHC); 9. Rodent; 10. Dry ice;
11. Copper and tin; 12. Kookaburra

WEATHER WISE

1. Rainfall; 2. Cirrus; 3. Eight; 4. Winds; 5. Air pressure;
6. Anti-cyclone; 7. Intensity of an earthquake; 8. First weather
satellite (TIROS 1); 9. Katrina; 10. Counter-clockwise;
11. The vapour content of air; 12. El Niño

MORE PLANTS AND TREES

1. Grass; 2. Japan; 3. Sphagnum; 4. New Zealand; 5. Sepal;
6. Sweet Chestnut; 7. Chinese Gooseberry; 8. Daffodil; 9. Fungus;
10. Its bark; 11. Stigma; 12. Africa

FURTHER AMONG THE ANIMALS

1. In its tail; 2. Calf; 3. Honeybee; 4. Rodent; 5. Mauritius;
6. Velvet; 7. Five; 8. Wolf; 9. Dog; 10. Elk; 11. Otter's;
12. Manatee

ANSWERS
SCIENCE & NATURE

....

RANDOM SAMPLE (3)
....

1. Hatchling; 2. Tuberculosis; 3. Rabbits; 4. Ice;
5. Vitamin D; 6. X-ray; 7. Laughing gas; 8. Nuclear energy;
9. Hypertext Mark-up Language; 10. 22; 11. Chrysalis; 12. Hydrogen

MAXI AND MINI
....

1. Cheetah; 2. Condor; 3. Diplodocus; 4. Blue whale; 5. African;
6. Mayfly; 7. Jackfruit; 8. Sloth; 9. Reticulated python; 10. Komodo
dragon; 11. Chan's Megastick (stick insect); 12. Peregrine falcon

MEDICAL MATTERS
....

1. Hippocrates; 2. Skull; 3. Mumps; 4. Chicken-pox;
5. Quinine; 6. Christiaan Barnard; 7. 1978; 8. CAT scan;
9. Heart attack; 10. Plaster of Paris; 11. Color blindness; 12. Foxglove

THE UNIVERSE
....

1. The Hubble; 2. Jupiter; 3. Exploding star; 4. Boiling; 5. Hale-Bopp;
6. The Sun; 7. Andromeda; 8. Hydrogen; 9. Eight minutes (approx);
10. Venus; 11. The Moon; 12. *Aurora borealis*

RANDOM SAMPLE (4)
....

1. Chlorophyll; 2. Rabies; 3. On its toes; 4. Snake; 5. Moth; 6. Minus 18°;
7. Nitrogen; 8. San Francisco; 9. Frequency Modulated;
10. J Robert Oppenheimer; 11. Vitamin C; 12. Dolly

ANSWERS

SCIENCE & NATURE

....

MORE OF THE HUMAN BODY
....

1. Ear (stapedius); 2. Voice box; 3. Cornea; 4. 100,000;
5. Fontanelles; 6. Outermost layer of the skin; 7.Tip; 8. Incisors,
Canines, Molars; 9. Muscle (back); 10. Hearing; 11. Ulna nerve;
12. Tooth enamel

....

GIANTS OF SCIENCE
....

1. Marie and Pierre Curie; 2. Isaac Newton; 3. Joseph Priestley;
4. Penicillin; 5. Sigmund Freud; 6. Edward Jenner; 7. Galileo Galilei;
8. Ernest Rutherford; 9. William Harvey; 10. Joseph Lister;
11. His theory of relativity; 12. Polish

....

PHOBIAS : WHAT ARE YOU AFRAID OF?
....

1. Cats; 2. Foreigners; 3. Speed; 4. Spiders; 5. Computers;
6. Marriage; 7. Bees; 8. Horses; 9. Water; 10. Strong light;
11. Being stared at; 12. Fear of becoming phobic

....

RANDOM SAMPLE (5)
....

1. Drey; 2. Mercury; 3. Digital Versatile Disc; 4. Head;
5. Royal Observatory, Greenwich; 6. Holt; 7. Carbon; 8. Bear;
9. Samuel Morse; 10. Whale Shark; 11. Egypt; 12. Birds

....

ANSWERS

SCIENCE & NATURE

STRANGE BUT TRUE

1. To mate with virgin queens; 2. Human flea; 3. Barnacle;
4. Newfoundland; 5. Mudskipper; 6. Jellyfish; 7. Seabirds; 8. Eight;
9. Seahorse; 10. Blowfly (bluebottle); 11. Electric eel; 12. Their wings

GREAT INVENTORS

1. John Logie Baird; 2. World Wide Web; 3. George Stephenson;
4. Turbo-jet engine; 5. Samuel Colt; 6. Hovercraft; 7. Guglielmo
Marconi; 8. The pencil; 9. Johannes Gutenberg's (printing press);
10. King Camp Gillette; 11. Daniel Fahrenheit; 12. Polaroid

WHAT WOULD YOU BE STUDYING?

1. Volcanoes; 2. Insects; 3. Feet; 4. Earthquakes; 5. Shells;
6. Whales and dolphins; 7. Ears; 8. Early humans; 9. Clouds;
10. Weights and measures; 11. The sun; 12. Rain

RANDOM SAMPLE (6)

1. Marsupial; 2. Electrical resistance; 3. Structure of DNA;
4. Owl; 5. Sirius; 6. Trees; 7. Leveret; 8. Sn; 9. Stethoscope;
10. Dandelion; 11. Potato; 12. Iceberg

ANSWERS
SPORTS & GAMES

....

SPORTING CHANCE (1)

....

1. Baseball; 2. Boxer Bob Fitzsimmons (1902); 3. 26; 4. Chess;
5. Astronaut Alan Shepard (1971); 6. Graham and Damon Hill;
7. Diane Leather; 8. Water skiing; 9. Crossbow (bolt); 10. 1964;
11. 15; 12. Antwerp

....

BASEBALL: 1ST INNINGS

....

1. Alexander Cartwright; 2. George Herman Ruth; 3. 1903;
4. Phil Niekro; 5. Yogi Berra; 6. A curveball; 7. Jackie Robinson;
8. Boston Red Sox; 9. 1939; 10. Arizona Diamondbacks;
11. 1992; 12. Ty Cobb

....

FOOTBALL: 1ST PLAY

....

1. 1967; 2. Vince Lombardi; 3. Pentathlon and Decathlon;
4. Jerome "The Bus" Bettis who retired then; 5. Curly Lambeau;
6. A pass thrown deep downfield; 7. Norway; 8. Syracuse;
9. Baltimore Colts v NY Giants (1958); 10. Joe Namath (in *The Waverly Wonders*); 11. Bart Starr; 12. The officials

....

GOLF: 1ST ROUND

....

1. Woods, irons, putters; 2. Two strokes under par on a hole;
3. Curtis Cup; 4. Italian; 5. Bob Charles; 6. Greg Norman;
7. Trevor Immelman; 8. 1927; 9. Karrie Webb; 10. Hole in one;
11. The Bronx in New York; 12. Byron Nelson

....

ANSWERS
SPORTS & GAMES

. . . .

BASKETBALL

. . . .

1. Harlem Globetrotters; 2. Australia; 3. Los Angeles (1984); 4. 1953;
5. Technical foul; 6. Philadelphia Warriors; 7. Converted peach
baskets; 8. Bob Cousy; 9. 7ft 7in (2.31m); 10. USSR (1972);
11. Shaquille O'Neal; 12. Argentina

. . . .

SPORTING CHANCE (2)

. . . .

1. Ice; 2. Pete Sampras; 3. Tom Lehman; 4. Wilheim Steinitz;
5. Begin; 6. Vikings; 7. John Davis; 8. Squash; 9. Rocky Graziano;
10. Team New Zealand; 11. Cycling; 12. Ohio State University

. . . .

MOTOR RACING: 1ST LAP

. . . .

1. 2006 (Hungarian); 2. San Marino; 3. Giuseppe Farina (1950);
4. That a faster car is trying to overtake; 5. Brazilian;
6. Driver error; 7. Le Mans; 8. Monza; 9. Jochen Rindt (who died
earlier in the season but never lost his lead); 10. Alain Prost;
11. 1911; 12. Phil Hill (1961)

. . . .

TENNIS: 1ST SET

. . . .

1. Jamie; 2. 3ft (0.914m); 3. 167; 4. Monica Seles; 5. Roche;
6. French Open; 7. Belgian; 8. Boris Becker (1985); 9. John Lloyd;
10. Spain; 11. Billie Jean Moffitt; 12. Four

. . . .

ANSWERS
SPORTS & GAMES

THE OLYMPICS

1. The five continents; 2. St Louis, 1904; 3. Ben Johnson;
4. 26 miles/42km; 5. Johnny Weissmuller (Tarzan in the movies) won
five for swimming; 6. Because of the USSR's invasion of Hungary;
7. Chamonix (France), 1924; 8. 100m, 200m, long jump, 4 x 100m
relay; 9. Nadia Comaneci; 10. 1960 (Rome); 11. Dutch athlete Fanny
Blankers-Koen; 12. Silver

SPORTING CHANCE (3)

1. Ernie Els; 2. Brazilian; 3. Winners of the NFL Super Bowl;
4. Basketball; 5. Two; 6. 18 inches; 7. Seven weeks; 8. Clay;
9. Thailand; 10. Rook; 11. 1999; 12. Evander Holyfield's

WHICH SPORTS FEATURED IN THESE MOVIES?

1. Baseball; 2. Baseball; 3. Equestrian; 4. Ice hockey;
5. Football; 6. Cycling; 7. Boxing; 8. Basketball; 9. Surfing;
10. Horse racing; 11. Basketball; 12. Athletics

BASEBALL: 2ND INNINGS

1. Walter Johnson; 2. 1919; 3. New York Yankees; 4. He was the
shortest-ever major-league player; 5. Gene Autry; 6. Cal Ripken Jr;
7. Striking out four times in a game; 8. All-American Girls
Professional Baseball League; 9. Hank Aaron; 10. Seven;
11. Being born without a right hand; 12. John Goodman

ANSWERS
SPORTS & GAMES

....

FOOTBALL: 2ND PLAY

....

1. Lions; 2. O J Simpson; 3. Jim Thorpe; 4. Dick Lane;
5. Both went to college on a football scholarship; 6. Green Bay Packers;
7. London Monarchs; 8. George Blanda (26); 9. 1970; 10. South Africa;
11. Plane crash; 12. Buffalo Bills', who won 41-38 after trailing 35-3

....

SPORTING CHANCE (4)

....

1. Figure skating; 2. Bully-off; 3. Steve Cauthen; 4. Shuttlecock;
5. Twins; 6. Twice; 7. Japan (1987); 8. John McEnroe;
9. Feathers of an arrow; 10. Fencing; 11. 1968; 12. Wrestling

....

GOLF: 2ND ROUND

....

1. St Andrews; 2. Newport (Rhode Island); 3. 14; 4. Gary Player (1961);
5. 1979; 6. Albatross; 7. Arnold Palmer; 8. Philadelphia Cricket Club;
9. Harry Vardon; 10. 1930; 11. Padraig Harrington;
12. Greenland

....

HOCKEY

....

1. Six; 2. A defenseman; 3. Great Britain; 4. The Canada Cup;
5. The NHL Most Valuable Player of the Year; 6. Mario Lemieux;
7. Montreal (1875); 8. Jaromir Jagr; 9. The Stanley Cup;
10. Philadelphia Flyers; 11. Gordie Howe; 12. Sweden

....

ANSWERS
SPORTS & GAMES

....

PLAYING GAMES

....

1. 18; 2. Allison Fisher; 3. Cardinal (the rest are chess pieces);
4. Uruguay; 5. 64; 6. Bridge; 7. Mah Jong; 8. Royal Flush;
9. Vladimir Kramnik; 10. 13 tricks by one team; 11. 15;
12. Backgammon

....

SPORTING CHANCE (5)

....

1. One and a quarter miles; 2. High jump; 3. Three; 4. 1903;
5. Swimming stroke; 6. 1994; 7. Harold Abrahams and Eric Liddell;
8. Logs; 9. Wrestling hold; 10. Oxford v Cambridge Boat Race;
11. Mark Spitz; 12. Michael Campbell's

....

NAME THE SPORT ASSOCIATED WITH THESE VENUES

....

1. Basketball; 2. Baseball; 3. Football; 4. Boxing; 5. Golf;
6. Ice hockey; 7. Car racing; 8. Golf; 9. Basketball; 10. Golf;
11. Baseball; 12. Tennis

....

CAR RACING: 2ND LAP

....

1. John Surtees; 2. South African; 3. Lotus; 4. Mario Andretti;
5. Six-wheeled car; 6. Sebring, Florida; 7. Tom Kristensen;
8. 0.043 of a second; 9. Indianapolis 500; 10. Shanghai; 11. Benetton;
12. Janet Guthrie

....

ANSWERS
SPORTS & GAMES

....

TENNIS: 2ND SET
....

1. Helen Wills Moody; 2. French Open (1956); 3. Eight years (1974 and 1982); 4. Ivan Lendl; 5. George VI (when Duke of York); 6. Rod Laver (1962, 1969); 7. Pete Sampras; 8. Evonne Goolagong; 9. Mark Philippoussis; 10. Tracy Austin; 11. Bill Tilden; 12. Cypriot

....

BOXING
....

1. Primo Carnera; 2. 49; 3. Joe Calzaghe; 4. Five; 5. Ezzard Charles; 6. Strawweight (or mini flyweight); 7. Frank Bruno; 8. Jersey Joe Walcott's; 9. Win titles in three different weight classes; 10. Plane crash; 11. Canada; 12. "Prince" Naseem Hamed

....

SPORTING CHANCE (6)
....

1. The America's Cup (1851); 2. Home run; 3. Zola Budd; 4. Jaroslav Drobny; 5. Show-jumping obstacle; 6. 1997; 7. Spain; 8. Swim the English Channel from France to England; 9. Marquess of Queensberry's; 10. Polo; 11. Oval; 12. Martina Hingis

....

ANSWERS
GENERAL KNOWLEDGE

· ·

NUMBER 1

· ·

1. Electrocardiogram; 2. 1948; 3. New Zealand; 4. 73; 5. Cardinals;
6. Isle of Man; 7. Mothballs; 8. Tooth decay; 9. Cointreau;
10. Vibraphone; 11. Nat Turner; 12. Paul

NUMBER 2

· ·

1. Sulfur; 2. 18; 3. Lady Godiva; 4. Red; 5. Topiary; 6. Tomato;
7. Twilight of the Gods; 8. Erica Jong; 9. San Andreas;
10. Knitting stitches; 11. Felix; 12. Yahoo

NUMBER 3

· ·

1. Lily; 2. Edith Cresson; 3. Half sister; 4. He was shot; 5. None;
6. Howard Hughes; 7. Advocaat; 8. Champion; 9. 1200;
10. Václav Havel (Czechoslovakia); 11. Pegasus;
12. Winnie Mandela

NUMBER 4

· ·

1. Comma; 2. Tashkent; 3. 28; 4. Delft; 5. Caspar, Balthasar, Melchior;
6. Lee; 7. Betty Ford; 8. Jacques Chirac; 9. Edmonton; 10. Bell-ringing;
11. Gregorian; 12. Divine wind

ANSWERS
GENERAL KNOWLEDGE

NUMBER 5

1. Jenny Shipley; 2. K; 3. Abigail; 4. Sign language; 5. Sheriff of Nottingham; 6. Chinese Mandarin; 7. Broadway; 8. Bulldog; 9. Lionel Stander; 10. River Tiber; 11. "The People's Car"; 12. Conquest, War, Famine, Death

NUMBER 6

1. 27; 2. Stalagmites; 3. North Atlantic; 4. Malcolm Maclaren; 5. Spanish Riding School; 6. Infallible; 7. Knot; 8. John Garfield; 9. Felix Salten; 10. Boat; 11. Diahann Carrol; 12. Turin

NUMBER 7

1. Very Superior Old Pale; 2. Christopher Isherwood's; 3. Twiggy; 4. Black; 5. Mob; 6. Benjamin Franklin; 7. Amritsar; 8. Peter Tchaikovsky; 9. Bad Homburg (homburg hat); 10. Simon and Garfunkel; 11. H; 12. Ten

NUMBER 8

1. Chemistry, Economics, Literature, Medicine, Peace, Physics; 2. Their letters are in alphabetical order; 3. Rob Petrie; 4. Statue of Zeus; 5. Vincent van Gogh; 6. Hendrik Verwoerd; 7. Giant Panda; 8. Nikolai Gogol; 9. Fibre-optic Link Around the Globe; 10. Kukri; 11. Bobby Darin; 12. St Fiacre

ANSWERS
GENERAL KNOWLEDGE

NUMBER 9

1. "Angel of Death"; 2. Cruz; 3. Tanzania; 4. Banknotes;
5. Captain James Cook; 6. John Carpenter; 7. Hats; 8. Swiss Guard;
9. Adam and the Ants; 10. Donald Duck's nephews; 11. Wednesday;
12. Both

NUMBER 10

1. Nebuchadnezzar; 2. Four; 3. Jawaharlal Nehru; 4. Phil Mickelson;
5. Japan; 6. Horse; 7. Peter Parker; 8. France's; 9. Model T Ford car;
10. N; 11. Study of words; 12. Yom Kippur

NUMBER 11

1. 150; 2. 1912; 3. Buddha; 4. Drunk; 5. Tennessee; 6. Richard Burton;
7. E M Forster; 8. St Petersburg; 9. Andorra, Belgium, Germany, Italy,
Luxembourg, Monaco, Spain, Switzerland; 10. Bolero; 11. Four;
12. Jimmy Carter's

NUMBER 12

1. Phineas T Barnum; 2. Donkey; 3. The pope; 4. Karl Marx and
Friedrich Engels; 5. Mesopotamia; 6. Zero Mostel; 7. Ennio Morricone;
8. A Passion Play; 9. Toad; 10. Belshazzar; 11. Fatted goose liver;
12. Obituaries

ANSWERS
GENERAL KNOWLEDGE

. . . .

NUMBER 13

. . . .

1. Imitation gold; 2. Napoleon Bonaparte; 3. Elephant; 4. Plane crash;
5. The ear; 6. One-sixth; 7. Anne Tyler; 8. Monkey; 9. Potato;
10. Benjamin Britten; 11. Mae West; 12. Marilyn Monroe

NUMBER 14

. . . .

1. Aardvark; 2. Petrograd and Leningrad; 3. Two hours;
4. Aleutian Islands; 5. Nazi Party; 6. Islamabad; 7. Quotient;
8. Bugs Bunny's; 9. Omega; 10. Aries; 11. Fifth; 12. Trampolining

NUMBER 15

. . . .

1. The Gambia; 2. *The Hunchback of Notre Dame*; 3. Munich;
4. "Thou Shalt Not Kill"; 5. Four; 6. Fractions; 7. "Boy"; 8. Five;
9. Chip Taylor; 10. Trade; 11. Jerome David; 12. La Bourse

NUMBER 16

. . . .

1. Edith Piaf; 2. *The Satanic Verses*; 3. *The Great Dictator*;
4. The Taoiseach; 5. Nimbus; 6. 1953; 7. Orange;
8. Worms; 9. Cresta Run; 10. Jean-Baptiste Molière; 11. Four;
12. Flower arranging

ANSWERS
GENERAL KNOWLEDGE

· ·

NUMBER 17

· ·

1. Arizona; 2. Nana; 3. Lentils; 4. Dag Hammarskjöld; 5. Phidias;
6. Randy "The Ram" Robinson; 7. Montevideo; 8. Ireland; 9. Shell;
10. Bram Stoker; 11. Three; 12. Jay

NUMBER 18

· ·

1. Halley's Comet; 2. John Major; 3. *Victor Victoria*;
4. Eleanor Roosevelt; 5. Jezebel; 6. John Milton; 7. Surfing; 8. 12;
9. Erich Maria Remarque; 10. Hanoi; 11. Stephen Frears;
12. In a church

NUMBER 19

· ·

1. Save Our Souls; 2. Top hat; 3. Palace of Versailles;
4. Westminster Abbey; 5. Miller; 6. Washington Irving;
7. Three Musketeers; 8. Advocaat; 9. Bing Crosby; 10. William Perry;
11. Eminem; 12. William Wordsworth and Samuel Taylor Coleridge

NUMBER 20

· ·

1. Danny Kaye; 2. Chantilly; 3. The Blue Peter; 4. Nucleus; 5. 1919;
6. March; 7. Right; 8. Yaddo; 9. 336; 10. The house;
11. Doris Lessing; 12. Marvin Hamlisch

ANSWERS
GENERAL KNOWLEDGE

NUMBER 21

1. *1984*; 2. Battle of the Bulge; 3. Margot Fonteyn; 4. Milwaukee;
5. Hawser; 6. Hermit crab; 7. The Three Graces; 8. St Mark;
9. Kim Il-sung; 10. Ali G; 11. Dan Quayle; 12. Sir Humphrey Davy

NUMBER 22

1. US Marine Corps; 2. Schultz; 3. Ra; 4. Booth Tarkington;
5. Bahrain; 6. Allen Ginsberg; 7. Owen Wister; 8. Yellow; 9. Brian Cox;
10. Damascus; 11. Fish; 12. Catalonia

NUMBER 23

1. Las Malvinas; 2. Butt; 3. Los Angeles Lakers; 4. Tides; 5. *Aida*;
6. Raven; 7. Elton John; 8. Rudyard Kipling's (*Just So Stories*);
9. Edward Gibbon; 10. Knights Templar; 11. Fishing flies; 12. 1970

NUMBER 24

1. Climbing plant; 2. Revelation; 3. Gross Domestic Product;
4. Cubism; 5. Ivy League; 6. 7/10th; 7. Cyrillic alphabet;
8. Geoffrey Rush; 9. Knights of the Round Table; 10. Judo (belt);
11. Green with red spots; 12. Twice cooked